SEVENTEEN
STEPS
TO 221B

Other titles available from Otto Penzler's
Sherlock Holmes Library:

The Private Life of Sherlock Holmes
by Vincent Starrett

Sherlock Holmes: Fact or Fiction?
by T. S. Blakeney

221B: Studies in Sherlock Holmes
Edited by Vincent Starrett

R. Holmes & Co.
by John Kendrick Bangs

My Dear Holmes: Studies in Sherlock
by Gavin Brend

Also by James Edward Holroyd

Baker Street Byways

The Gaslight Murders

Baker Street as it was in Holmes' and Watson's day.

SEVENTEEN STEPS TO 221B

A SHERLOCKIAN COLLECTION BY
ENGLISH WRITERS

WITH AN INTRODUCTION BY
JAMES EDWARD HOLROYD

OTTO
PENZLER
BOOKS

NEW YORK

Otto Penzler Books
129 West 56th Street
New York, NY 10019
(Editorial Offices only)

Macmillan Publishing Company
866 Third Avenue
New York, NY 10022

Maxwell Macmillan Canada, Inc.
1200 Eglinton Avenue East, Suite 200
Don Mills, Ontario M3C 3N1

Macmillan Publishing Company is part of the Maxwell Communication Group of Companies.

Library of Congress Cataloging-in-Publication Data
Seventeen steps to 221B : a Sherlockian collection / by English writers; with an introduction by James Edward Holroyd.
    p.   cm.
  Originally published: London: G. Allen & Unwin, c1967.
  ISBN 1-883402-72-7
  1. Doyle, Arthur Conan, Sir, 1859–1930—Characters—Sherlock Holmes. 2. Detective and mystery stories, English—History and criticism. 3. Holmes, Sherlock (Fictitious character). 4. Private investigators in literature. I. Holroyd, James Edward.
PR4624.S4   1994   93-42879   CIP
823'.8—dc20

Otto Penzler Books are available at special discounts for bulk purchases for sales promotions, premiums, fund-raising, or educational use. For details, contact:

Special Sales Director
Macmillan Publishing Company
866 Third Avenue
New York, NY 10022

10 9 8 7 6 5 4 3 2 1

Printed in the United States of America

ACKNOWLEDGMENTS

Grateful thanks are extended to the Trustees of the Conan Doyle Estate for approving the publication of this collection.

Gerald Duckworth and Co. Ltd. for 'From the Diary of Sherlock Holmes' from *Lost Diaries* by Maurice Baring.

Mr C. R. Milne and Methuen and Co. Ltd. for 'Dr Watson Speaks Out' from *By Way of Introduction* by A. A. Milne.

The Literary Executor and Sheed and Ward Ltd. for 'Studies in the Literature of Sherlock Holmes' from *Essays in Satire* by Mgr. R. A. Knox.

The Executors of the late Sir Sydney Roberts and Oxford University Press for 'The Chronological Problem' from *Holmes and Watson: a Miscellany*.

Lady Rachel Cecil and MacGibbon and Kee for 'Dr Watson' from *Memories* by Sir Desmond MacCarthy.

Victor Gollancz for 'The Dates in The Red-Headed League' from *Unpopular Opinions* by Dorothy Sayers.

Arthur Marshall and the *New Statesman* for 'Ring for our Boots'.

Sir Robin Darwin and Collins Ltd. for 'Sherlockiana: The Faith of a Fundamentalist' from *Every Idle Dream* by Bernard Darwin.

E. V. Knox and George Newnes Ltd. for 'The Passing of Sherlock Holmes' from *The Strand*, 1948.

Sir John Masterman, the *Evening Standard* and Hodder and Stoughton for 'The Case of the Gifted Amateur' from *Bits and Pieces*.

Mrs Phyllis Brend and the *Sherlock Holmes Journal* for 'The Route of the Blue Carbuncle'.

Adrian Conan Doyle and John Murray (Publishers) Ltd. for 'The Deptford Horror' from *The Exploits of Sherlock Holmes*.

John Dickson Carr and Whitbreads Ltd. for 'Another Glass, Watson'.

The editor of the *Cornhill* and John Murray (Publishers) Ltd. for 'Our Client's Foot upon the Stair'.

ACKNOWLEDGMENTS

Dr W. C. Bristowe and the *Sherlock Holmes Journal* for 'The Truth about Moriarty'.

Lord Donegall and the *New Strand* for 'April 1891–April 1894'.

Bernard Davies and the *Sherlock Holmes Journal* for 'Backyards of Baker Street'.

Mrs Margaret Gunn and the *Sherlock Holmes Journal* for the examination paper.

ILLUSTRATIONS

1, 7. *A London Reverie* by J. C. Squire and Joseph Pennell (Macmillan and Co. Ltd., 1928)

2. *Radio Times* Hulton Picture Library

3. *From Charing Cross to St Paul's* by Justin McCarthy and Joseph Pennell (Seeley and Co. Ltd., 1893)

4. (a) *Living London* edited by George R. Sims (Cassell and Co. Ltd., 1900?)

   (b) George Newnes Ltd. and the *Cornhill*

5, 6. *The Queen's London* (Cassell and Co. Ltd., 1897)

CONTENTS

ACKNOWLEDGMENTS *page* 7

INTRODUCTION 13

1. *From the Diary of Sherlock Holmes* 21
MAURICE BARING

2. *Dr Watson Speaks Out* 25
A. A. MILNE

3. *Studies in the Literature of Sherlock Holmes* 30
RONALD KNOX

4. *The Chronological Problem* 46
S. C. ROBERTS

5. *Dr Watson* 50
DESMOND MACCARTHY

6. *The Dates in* The Red-Headed League 57
DOROTHY L. SAYERS

7. *'Ring for our Boots'* 68
ARTHUR MARSHALL

8. *Sherlockiana: The Faith of a Fundamentalist* 74
BERNARD DARWIN

9. *The Passing of Sherlock Holmes* 82
E. V. KNOX

10. *The Case of the Gifted Amateur* 90
J. C. MASTERMAN

11. *The Route of the Blue Carbuncle* 100
GAVIN BREND

CONTENTS

12. *The Adventure of the Deptford Horror*   *page* 106
    ADRIAN CONAN DOYLE

13. *'Another Glass, Watson!'*   126
    JOHN DICKSON CARR

14. *'Our Client's Foot upon the Stair'*   132
    JAMES EDWARD HOLROYD

15. *The Truth about Moriarty*   144
    W. C. BRISTOWE

16. *April 1891–April 1894*   161
    LORD DONEGALL

17. *Back Yards of Baker Street*   167
    BERNARD DAVIES

ANNEX

Examination Paper   179
R. IVAR GUNN

ILLUSTRATIONS

> ⟶ ✿✿ ⟵

1. Baker Street in Holmes' day   *frontispiece*

2. Oxford Circus in 1888   *facing page* 32

3. The Lyceum Theatre, Wellington
   Street, Strand, at night   *facing page* 33

4. (*a*) The former long bar at the
       Criterion   *facing page* 80

   (*b*) Inside 221B Baker Street   *facing page* 80

5. The Strand, looking west   *facing page* 81

6. Piccadilly on a fine sunny morning   *facing page* 96

7. Fleet Street   *facing page* 97

INTRODUCTION

>→ ❊ ←

One morning during the last war, a distinguished civil servant on his way to the office was asked by a Canadian soldier if he would identify some of the London landmarks from Westminster Bridge. As guide and guided parted company at the corner of Parliament Square, the official pointed to the Abbey and St Margaret's. Then, with a final wave of the hand along White-hall, he said: 'And across the way, of course, we have Downing Street.' 'I know,' the soldier replied in suitably reverential tones, '—Sherlock Holmes!'

Although the topography was shaky, the visitor had struck the right cosmic note, for in North America alone there are around fifty societies devoted to Sherlock Holmes and his partner, Dr John H. Watson, late of the Army Medical Department.

As often as I am asked what makes the Baker Street movement tick, I reply that it is part escapism, part the desire to indulge in a little amateur detective work oneself. Both are obvious attractions. To re-read the sixty adventures that comprise the Baker Street saga is to evoke snug echoes of a vanished era, largely untroubled by the internal combustion engine, totally unshadowed by the bomb. It is, I suppose, like journeying back towards the serenity and security of childhood.

But this nostalgia would not of itself sustain the world-wide appeal of the great detective and his partner. I believe that a large part of the perennial fascination lies in attempting to reconcile the inconsistencies encountered in the adventures. In this exercise, Sherlockians have some common ground with Dickensians; but whereas devotees of Doughty Street are more or less limited to Edwin Drood as the major unsolved mystery in the series, the Baker Street *aficionados* are apt to find a problem on every other page. What was the basis of Holmes' professional fees, which, we are told, were on a fixed scale, save when he remitted them altogether? Could Dr Watson have been the old campaigner he so frequently claimed to be? Was there another tenant at 221 B Baker Street? These are characteristic of the problems that keep students happily (and harmlessly) engaged all over the world.

One of the felicities of the Baker Street cult is that even the most cursory re-reading may point a new way to the solution of an old problem. For example, the question of Oxford or Cambridge as Holmes' university has been carefully, if inconclusively, debated by savants of such eminence as the late Mgr Knox, the late Dorothy Sayers, Lord Donegall and the late Sir Sydney Roberts, all of whom appear in this collection of Sherlockian pieces by English writers. When I recently glanced at *The Missing Three-quarter* for the nth time, a hitherto unremarked clue leapt out of the page. Holmes has just been told by his visitor that Godfrey Staunton, the Cambridge right-wing three-quarter—'the hinge that the whole team turns on'—has disappeared on the eve of the most important match of the year. He thereupon takes down the 'S' volume of his commonplace books. 'There is Arthur H. Staunton, the rising young forger,' said he, 'and there was Henry Staunton, whom I helped to hang, but Godfrey Staunton is a new name to me.' The fact that Holmes instinctively consulted his rogues' gallery when a Cambridge man was mentioned could be regarded as strong proof that he himself was at Oxford. Alas, the point is not decisive. Holmes' university experience might have been so unhappy that he would have reached for his criminal encyclopedia whichever foundation he had attended.

In *Baker Street By-ways* I suggested that Holmes' reasoning betrayed 'a slight tremor' when he deduced Henry Baker's intellect from the size of his hat and, from the grease-spots on it, that his home was not lit by gas. Here is a little more juice from the same orange. Because the abandoned goose had a card 'For Mrs Henry Baker' on its legend and the hat-band bore the initials 'H.B.', Holmes built up a wonderfully detailed picture of a man whose wife had ceased to love him, etc. etc. In fact, the owner of the hat could have been a bachelor named, say, Horace Baker or Homer Baker, the black sheep who had been invited to spend Christmas with his married brother and who was taking the bird along as a peace-offering to his sister-in-law, who disapproved of his convivial habits. There is nothing improbable in brothers having the same initial. One recalls that the initial of Dr John *H*. Watson's own elder brother (another happy wanderer type!) was 'H'. Holmes' lucky assumption in this Christmas story of *The Blue Carbuncle* proved to be correct. H.B. in fact turned out to be Henry Baker. But it is worth noting that while Watson as a rule was suitably astounded at Holmes' mental processes, on this occasion he merely remarked: 'Your reasoning is certainly plausible.' Does one detect a hint of reservation in the tone of voice? It was justified.

What also of the advertisement which was to be inserted in the *Globe, Star, Pall Mall, et al*? The draft ran to thirty words:

Found at the corner of Goodge Street, a goose and black felt hat. Mr Henry Baker can have the same by applying at 6.30 this evening at 221B Baker Street.

'That is clear and concise,' Holmes remarked complacently. As an inveterate sender of telegrams, however, he ought to have done much better. 'Henry Baker can collect his hat and goose from 221B Baker Street at 6.30 tonight' would have achieved the trick in half the wordage.

While enthusiasts delve gleefully into the numerous unresolved facets of the Baker Street *ménage*, the public image of Holmes and Watson grows larger with the years. Apart from many projections of their fame and fortune on television and sound radio, much has been written about the partnership in recent years. (There is a balanced account of their creation in Professor Pierre Nordon's definitive life of Sir Arthur Conan Doyle.) At Sadler's Wells they broke into a new dimension in a ballet. Last year a new colour film showed Holmes solving the mystery of Jack the Ripper and a musical entitled 'Baker Street' was staged in New York. Both of these more recent manifestations take liberties with the accepted saga. Thus, there is no canonical authority for the Ripper episode, although it certainly occurred during Holmes' active career as an investigator. In the musical there is a love scene between Holmes and Irene Adler—a development which devotees of the great misogynist regard askance. But at least the licence is taken in good company. For when William Gillette, the American actor, asked the author if he might introduce a love interest in the Sherlock Holmes play he produced at the turn of the century, Sir Arthur briskly cabled: 'Marry him, murder him, do what you like with him.' It should be recorded that some enthusiasts regarded even this high canonical (Conanical?) authority with disfavour.

Although jingling hansoms and gas-lit streets are no more, London pays homage to the world's greatest detective through the corpus of the Sherlock Holmes Society, which has steadily grown to a membership of upwards of 300. While loyalty continues undiminished, the society has had to acknowledge two casualties in the visible tributes to Holmes in the past few years. Nameplates, presented in 1953, were ceremonially returned when individual locomotives were discarded by London Transport. Around the same period the society was associated with the installation of a plaque outside the old Criterion Bar in Piccadilly Circus to commemorate Watson's meeting with the man who was to introduce him to Holmes. This votive tablet was the inspiration of the Tokyo chapter of the Baker Street Irregulars of New York. The plaque was mysteriously removed soon after installation. Several years elapsed before it was recovered and to date it has not yet been restored to its honoured site.

The remaining tributes to Holmes in London are a plaque in a laboratory at Bart's Hospital to commemorate the first meeting of the partners, a Sherlock Holmes bookcase in St Marylebone Reference Library, the manuscript of a Baker Street adventure in the British Museum, and, of course, the 'Sherlock Holmes' tavern in Northumberland Street, just off Trafalgar Square.

An associational item was exhibited at Bart's during the City of London Festival in 1966. Parties of visitors to see the plaque were shown an old-style lab stool, salvaged from a forgotten lumber-store, with the name 'Sherlock Holmes' and the appropriate date poker-burned on the back-rest. To the whole-hearted Sherlockian this appeared to confirm that Holmes had actually studied at Bart's. To the more sceptical it at least offered the possibility that some pioneer student had perpetuated this obscure tribute to Holmes, perhaps long before the current legend developed.

The 'Sherlock Holmes' tavern naturally remains the principal place of pilgrimage in London as its cosmopolitan visitors' book bears witness. The engraved portraits of Sir Arthur Conan Doyle and Dr Watson on the windows; the glass cases of exhibits in the bar; the twin portraits on the period sign; above all, the exact reproduction of the sitting room of 221 B Baker Street in the dining room upstairs—these together make up a nostalgic piece which is securely lodged in the affections of a multitude of admirers.

The proceedings at the 'Sherlock Holmes' are amiably described in John Dickson Carr's note in this collection. Much of the material displayed has been loaned by the Conan Doyle Estate and will eventually be installed in the castle at Lucens, in Switzerland, which Adrian Conan Doyle has converted into an international museum-memorial to his father and the Conan Doyle family. Meanwhile, both Sir Arthur and Holmes, with their flair for the picturesque, would no doubt have been flattered by the starry-eyed American visitor, who, having patiently worked his way round the show pieces in the bar, politely inquired: 'Is the Shakespearean room upstairs?'

As a footnote for those who are out of key with Sherlockian what-nottery, there is reassuring evidence that the Northumberland Street shrine is being 'watched'. Some time ago a stranger attracted attention by asking extremely pertinent questions. He afterwards left his card. The name was Moriarty.

The seventeen pieces of Sherlockiana assembled here illustrate the learned and/or light-hearted affection which has been given to the Baker Street legend by English writers during the past half-century. The title is an allusion to the number of steps leading up to the sitting-room at 221 B and was used by Holmes in *A Scandal in Bohemia* as an example of Watson's deficient powers of observation. The collection is not claimed to be more than representative; if it requires a justification it is that much of the material is not readily accessible otherwise. Footnotes in general are omitted. It will be obvious, for example, that Mgr Knox's study was written before the later volumes of the saga had appeared and that his brother's essay was published when Mr Attlee, now Lord Attlee, was Prime Minister.

The rough chronological sequence in which these tributes to

Holmes and Watson are set out fugitively reflects the onward sweep of interest in the affairs of Baker Street. Maurice Baring's skilful and good-humoured send-up was published in 1913, in the blessed period when new stories about Sherlock Holmes were still to be read in *The Strand Magazine*. Those eagerly awaited memoirs, mainly from the 'pen' of Dr Watson, continued intermittently until 1927. In the following year John Murray launched the omnibus edition of short stories—never out of print during the succeeding thirty-nine years.

In 1928 the late Mgr Ronald Knox also published *Essays in Satire* which included the renowned 'Studies in the Literature of Sherlock Holmes'. The late Sir Sydney Roberts, for many years Master of Pembroke College, Cambridge, and a former Vice-Chancellor of the University, reviewed the Knox essay in similarly mock-serious style. In the same year A. A. Milne revealed unsuspected frustrations in Dr Watson's character by his outspoken assessment of the short stories.

The late Sir Desmond MacCarthy's thumb-nail biography of Dr Watson was written in 1929, the same year as first publication of the companion omnibus of the four long Sherlock Holmes stories. Sir Arthur Conan Doyle died in 1930.

Several notable volumes of Sherlockiana were published during the early 1930s. The late Dorothy Sayers' ingenious analysis of *The Red-headed League* was apparently written in 1934, although she quoted contemporaneously from the chronology compiled by H. W. Bell, an American savant, which was published in 1932.

The original Sherlock Holmes Society of London, founded in 1934, met only for an annual dinner, did not survive the war, and did not record its proceedings in detail. But at any rate it provided a corpus of devotees to work out new solutions and correspond with their brethren in the United States where the cult was already proliferating. The war-time torch for the movement was in fact carried by the Americans. ('And not by eastern windows only . . .'?) Presidents Roosevelt and Truman both accepted membership of the Baker Street Irregulars of New York, while the code name of the US Office of Strategic Services Headquarters in London was 'Baker Street'.

The immediate post-war years brought such admirable contributions to Baker Street lore as Arthur Marshall's *New States-*

man essay, the late Bernard Darwin's 'Faith of a Fundamentalist', and E. V. Knox's *Times*-style obituary, all during
1948. (The faithful like to believe that Holmes is still living
in timeless retirement. But the Moriartys are still with us;
for *The Spectator* of June 20, 1952, reported that the advertisement department of *The Times* had recently accepted the
following announcement for insertion in the 'Deaths' column:
'HOLMES. On June 9, 1952, finally and peacefully at his home
in Sussex, Sherlock, brother of Mycroft.' The *Spectator* added
that the advertisement department took out the word 'finally'
on the grounds that it was redundant, 'but the announcement
[which had been paid for] would have appeared had it not
been spotted by a member of the editorial staff'.)

Sir John Masterman is a former Provost of Worcester College,
Oxford, and has written several thrillers in the best academic
tradition. His agreeable reminiscence of Inspector Lestrade, the
most familiar of the fourteen named detectives in the adventures,
scores what must be one of the very few points the rat-faced and
ferret-like official was ever able to claim over his great protag-
onist. It was first published in 1950. The late Gavin Brend's
dutiful pacing of the route of the blue carbuncle was written
in 1957, and can be regarded as a pendant to his book-length
study *My Dear Holmes*.

It was in 1957 also that Adrian Conan Doyle published the
Exploits of Sherlock Holmes, a new collection of Baker Street
adventures based on casual references in the original canon.
Ingenuity of plot and fidelity to manner and period alike made
a notable landmark in Sherlockian literature. (It is pertinent to
hint that many similar adventures, to which Watson made only
the briefest and most tantalizing allusion, remain as yet untold:
they are stories for which the world is now eagerly prepared.)
Some of the *Exploits* were written in collaboration with John
Dickson Carr, who published *The Life of Sir Arthur Conan
Doyle* in 1949. His essay, reproduced here, is taken from the
Whitbread catalogue of the 'Sherlock Holmes' tavern.

The piece by Lord Donegall appeared in the *New Strand* and
those by Dr Bristowe, Bernard Davies and the late R. Ivar
Gunn in the *Sherlock Holmes Journal* in recent years. They
demonstrate that the zest and the opportunity for companion-
able research do not diminish.

Lord Donegall edits the journal for the Sherlock Holmes Society of London. Its opposite number is the *Baker Street Journal* of New York, edited by Dr Julian Wolff. These are the dual poles of a friendly but independent axis dedicated to rewarding (if unremitting) study of the immortal partnership. They recall the tribute that Brother Mycroft paid to Dr Watson on a long-ago summer's evening at the Diogenes Club in Pall Mall: 'I hear of Sherlock everywhere since you became his chronicler.'

MAURICE BARING

FROM THE DIARY OF
SHERLOCK HOLMES

Baker Street, January 1. Starting a diary in order to jot down a few useful incidents which will be of no use to Watson. Watson very often fails to see that an unsuccessful case is more interesting from a professional point of view than a successful case. He means well.

January 6. Watson has gone to Brighton for a few days, for change of air. This morning quite an interesting little incident happened which I note as a useful example of how sometimes people who have no powers of deduction nevertheless stumble on the truth for the wrong reason. (This never happens to Watson, *fortunately.*) Lestrade called from Scotland Yard with reference to the theft of a diamond and ruby ring from Lady Dorothy Smith's wedding presents. The facts of the case were briefly these: On Thursday evening such of the presents as were jewels had been brought down from Lady Dorothy's bedroom to the drawing-room to be shown to an admiring group of friends. The ring was amongst them. After they had been shown, the jewels were taken upstairs once more and locked in the safe. The next morning the ring was missing. Lestrade, after investigating the matter, came to the conclusion that the ring had not been stolen, but had either been dropped in the drawing-room, or replaced in one of the other cases; but since he had searched the room and the remaining cases, his theory so far received no support. I accompanied him to Eaton Square to the residence of Lady Middlesex, Lady Dorothy's mother.

While we were engaged in searching the drawing-room, Lestrade uttered a cry of triumph and produced the ring from the lining of the arm chair. I told him he might enjoy the

21

triumph, but that the matter was not quite so simple as he seemed to think. A glance at the ring had shown me not only that the stones were false, but that the false ring had been made in a hurry. To deduce the name of its maker was of course child's play. Lestrade or any pupil of Scotland Yard would have taken for granted it was the same jeweller who had made the real ring. I asked for the bridegroom's present, and in a short time I was interviewing the jeweller who had provided it. As I thought, he had made a ring, with imitation stones (made of the dust of real stones), a week ago, for a young lady. She had given no name and had fetched and paid for it herself. I deduced the obvious fact that Lady Dorothy had lost the real ring, her uncle's gift, and, not daring to say so, had had an imitation ring made. I returned to the house, where I found Lestrade, who had called to make arrangements for watching the presents during their exhibition.

I asked for Lady Dorothy, who at once said to me:

'The ring was found yesterday by Mr Lestrade.'

'I know,' I answered, 'but which ring?'

She could not repress a slight twitch of the eyelids as she said: 'There was only one ring.'

I told her of my discovery and of my investigations.

'This is a very odd coincidence, Mr Holmes,' she said. 'Someone else must have ordered an imitation. But you shall examine my ring for yourself.' Whereupon she fetched the ring, and I saw it was no imitation. She had of course in the meantime found the real ring.

But to my intense annoyance she took it to Lestrade and said to him:

'Isn't this the ring you found yesterday, Mr Lestrade?'

Lestrade examined it and said, 'Of course, it is absolutely identical in every respect.'

'And do you think it is an imitation?' asked this most provoking young lady.

'Certainly not,' said Lestrade, and turning to me he added: 'Ah! Holmes, that is where theory leads one. At the Yard we go in for facts.'

I could say nothing; but as I said good-bye to Lady Dorothy I congratulated her on having found the real ring. The incident, although it proved the correctness of my reasoning, was vexing as it gave that ignorant blunderer an opportunity of crowing over me.

January 10. A man called just as Watson and I were having breakfast. He didn't give his name. He asked me if I knew who he was. I said, 'Beyond seeing that you are unmarried, that you have travelled up this morning from Sussex, that you have served in the French Army, that you write for reviews, and are especially interested in the battles of the Middle Ages, that you give lectures, that you are a Roman Catholic, and that you have once been to Japan, I don't know who you are.'

The man replied that he *was* unmarried, but that he lived in Manchester, that he had never been to Sussex or Japan, that he had never written a line in his life, that he had never served in any army save the English Territorial force, that so far from being a Roman Catholic he was a Freemason, and that he was by trade an electrical engineer—I suspected him of lying; and I asked him why his boots were covered with the clayey and chalk mixture peculiar to Horsham; why his boots were French Army service boots, elastic-sided, and bought probably at Valmy; why the second half of a return ticket from Southwater was emerging from his ticket-pocket; why he wore the medal of St Anthony on his watch-chain; why he smoked Caporal cigarettes; why the proofs of an article on the Battle of Eylau were protruding from his breast-pocket, together with a copy of the *Tablet*; why he carried in his hand a parcel which, owing to the untidy way in which it had been made (an untidiness which, in harmony with the rest of his clothes, showed that he could not be married) revealed the fact that it contained photographic magic lantern slides; and why he was tattooed on the left wrist with a Japanese fish.

'The reason I have come to consult you will explain some of these things,' he answered.

'I was staying last night at the Windsor Hotel, and this morning when I woke up I found an entirely different set of clothes from my own. I called the waiter and pointed this out, but neither the waiter nor any of the other servants, after making full inquiries, were able to account for the change. None of the other occupants of the hotel had complained of anything being wrong with their own clothes.

'Two gentlemen had gone out early from the hotel at 7.30.

One of them had left for good, the other was expected to return.

'All the belongings I am wearing, including this parcel, which contains slides, belong to someone else.

'My own things contained nothing valuable, and consisted of clothes and boots very similar to these; my coat was also stuffed with papers. As to the tattoo, it was done at a Turkish bath by a shampooer, who learnt the trick in the Navy.'

The case did not present any features of the slightest interest. I merely advised the man to return to the hotel and await the real owner of the clothes, who was evidently the man who had gone out at 7.30.

This is a case of my reasoning being, with one partial exception, perfectly correct. Everything I had deduced would no doubt have fitted the real owner of the clothes.

Watson asked rather irrelevantly why I had not noticed that the clothes were not the man's own clothes.

A stupid question, as the clothes were reach-me-downs which fitted him as well as such clothes ever do fit, and he was probably of the same build as their rightful owner.

January 12. Found a carbuncle of unusual size in the plum-pudding. Suspected the makings of an interesting case. But luckily, before I had stated any hypothesis to Watson—who was greatly excited—Mrs Turner came in and noticed it and said her naughty nephew Bill had been at his tricks again, and that the red stone had come from a Christmas tree. Of course, I had not examined the stone with my lens.

2

A. A. MILNE

DR WATSON SPEAKS OUT

The suggestion of the Editor of *The Nation* that I should myself review in his paper the collected adventures of my friend Mr Sherlock Holmes, which, it will be remembered, I was the first to lay before the public, comes at an opportune moment; for though I am a man of even temperament (save when the weather adversely affects my old wound) I am not one who can sit down under injustice, and in the matter of this book I feel that a grave wrong had been done to me. In order to explain just what this is I must take the public into my confidence in a way that only became necessary in the March of this year, when, as will be remembered, Inspector Lestrade fell off the pier at Southend when the tide was unfortunately out, and suffered a dislocation of the cervical vertebrae which has delayed, if not actually restricted, the memoirs which he had proposed to publish. In those memoirs, as I understand from his widow, he would have done me the justice which a mistaken sense of loyalty to my friend Mr Holmes has hitherto prevented me doing to myself.

In the course of my different narratives I have had occasion to refer from time to time to a medical practice which I had purchased at Paddington. The real truth about this practice has not yet come to light, for the various small deceptions in regard to it which I played upon my friend Holmes (always an easy man to deceive) have undoubtedly led both him and the public to suppose it other than it actually was. The truth which I am now at liberty to reveal is that the practice when I bought it consisted almost entirely of a Mrs Withers, and that the surprising death of Mrs Withers during my prolonged absence at Paisley in connection with the Syncopated Bacon Frauds left me with no means of subsistence other than an inadequate wound pension. In this predicament it was natural that I should look about for some other source of income.

I had always been fond of writing, and my descriptions of the Afghan Campaign as sent home in weekly letters to my Aunt Hester at Leamington, and by her submitted to the *Leamington Courier*, had received considerable editorial commendation, although, owing to the exigencies of space and an unexpected local interest in some trouble at the gas-works, they had been denied actual publication. In the hope that my pen had not lost its cunning, I now decided to write out in narrative form some of the adventures in which my friend Holmes and I had participated, and submit them to one of the more popular monthly magazines. Of the instantaneous success of my venture into literature I need not now speak, for it is public knowledge. But the means by which this success was achieved has remained obscure until today, when, in the regrettable absence of Inspector Lestrade, it has fallen to me to reveal it.

One of the most useful arts by which a writer may achieve his effects is the Art of Contrast. I remember that in my letters home during the Afghan Campaign (in which I received my wound) I often employed this art with telling effect; contrasting for instance, the sublimities of the mountain scenery, by which we were surrounded on all sides, with the occasional inadequacies of the sanitary arrangements; and so forth. So now, in my stories, I decided to heighten the effect by contrasting as sharply as possible the characters of Holmes and myself. Holmes is in many ways the most remarkable man I have met, but he was human. *Humanum est errare*, as my old anatomy lecturer used to say. Holmes was human enough to make mistakes, and human enough to resent their being found out. It became my habit, therefore, both in my personal relations with him, and in the narratives which I was putting before the public, to cover up, as far as possible, the very natural errors into which he fell, and to heighten the public appreciation of his amazing talent by contrasting it whenever possible with an assumed obtuseness of my own. It amuses me now to think how little he suspected this, just as it fills me with pride to think how greatly he, and through him the country, profited by it. For

Holmes was an artist, and, above all, an artist must believe continuously in his own powers.

Let me refer my readers to the story known as *The Disappearance of Lady Frances Carfax*. In this story, it will be remembered, I record how Holmes deduced from the appearance of my boots that I had just come back from a Turkish bath. It was a matter of habit with me by this time to admiringly admit the correctness of all his deductions, and to ask for the explanations which he was longing to give. The explanation in this case was that my boots were tied with an elaborate bow, such as only a bootmaker or a bath attendant would use; undoubtedly a keen piece of observation and an intelligent deduction. But he went on to say, 'It is unlikely that it is the bootmaker, since your boots are nearly new. Well, what remains? The bath.' Why, because one has a newish pair of boots, one should not buy a pair of slippers (as in fact I had been doing, having received a substantial cheque that morning from the Editor), why one should not even buy a second pair of boots, I do not know; but it was without difficulty, almost without conscious thought, that I replied, 'Holmes, you are wonderful.' It was on this same occasion that he deduced from the splashes on my left sleeve that I had sat on the left side of my hansom (which was true), and that, therefore, I must have had a companion (which was not true); for, like most men, I prefer to lean against the side of a cab rather than sit upright in the middle. But to have told Holmes so would have destroyed his confidence in himself, and to have told the public so would undoubtedly have detracted from the financial value of the stories. 'Holmes,' I said again, 'you are marvellous,' and he never suspected otherwise.

Undoubtedly his arrogance grew under my flattery, and sometimes this arrogance was hard to bear. It will be remembered that, in our inquiry into the curious experience of *The Retired Colourman*, it fell to me to undertake the preliminary investigations. I was giving Holmes some account of these, and describing with the minute particularity on which he insisted the state of a certain wall, 'mottled with lichens and topped with moss', as I put it, when he broke in rudely, 'Cut out the poetry, Watson. I note that it was a high brick wall.' Now it so happened that in an earlier inquiry into the extraordinary mystery of *The Decentralized Tomato* one of the cases which

I have not recorded, as being only notable for the reason that
Holmes was searching Newcastle for a tall left-handed man with
a red beard and long finger-nails at the very moment when
Lestrade was arresting the actual murderess at Brighton—in the
course of that inquiry Holmes himself had said to me, speaking
of the high brick wall behind the tomato-house, 'Tut tut,
Watson, the lichen. Does it suggest nothing to you?' And when I
had made some such obvious answer as that the wall seemed to
have been there a long time, he went on muttering to himself,
'Fool! The lichen! Why wasn't I told about the lichen?' It will
be seen, then, that my deliberate policy of humouring Holmes
was not without its undeserved humiliations.

My readers may ask why I should be taking the public into
my confidence now when I have put up with these humiliations
in silence for so long? The answer lies in the final collection of all
the stories into one volume. If my readers will turn to the last
section of the volume, entitled *The Case-Book of Sherlock Holmes*,
they will read there two stories, inferior stories if I may say
so without prejudice, written by Holmes himself. As a writer
who has taken himself seriously, even from those early Afghan
days, I do not object to belittling myself if by so doing I
can increase the artistic value of my narrative. But I can reasonably protest when another belittles me. Moreover, these two
stories were inserted into *The Case-Book* without my permission, and by collusion, I must suppose, between Holmes and the
publishers. I protested strongly at the time of the book's separate publication; I protest again strongly now. I have written
both to the Incorporated Society of Authors and to the British
Medical Council. I have also called the attention of Messrs
Murray to a demonstrably false statement in one of the stories,
which says, with all the circumstance of apparent truth, 'It was
in January 1903 . . . The good Watson had at that time
deserted me for a wife.' I married, as my readers know, in 1887,
and my poor wife died in the early 'nineties. For reasons into
which I need not go now I did not marry again. Already, as the
result of this false publication, I have had an inquiry from the
Income Tax Commissioners as to my second wife's independent
means, and a circular addressed to Mrs Watson calling attention to an alleged infallible method, obtained from an
unregistered and unqualified Indian sepoy, for removing

superfluous hairs. Is it any wonder that I am indignant?

I therefore solemnly call upon the publishers to withdraw the volume from circulation, even though I myself shall be the first to suffer financially by it. Fortunately I have enough now for my simple needs. With the proceeds of previous sales I have purchased another small practice (an elderly gentleman of arthritic tendencies called Ferguson), and with this and my wound pension (a relic of the Afghan Campaign) I am content. But if that content is to be disturbed by the continual circulation of false statements, then let me warn all concerned that I shall not take it lying down. *There are other revelations which I could make. . . .*

$$\twoheadrightarrow * \, 3 \, * \twoheadleftarrow$$

RONALD KNOX

STUDIES IN THE LITERATURE OF SHERLOCK HOLMES

If there is anything pleasant in life, it is doing what we aren't meant to do. If there is anything pleasant in criticism, it is finding out what we aren't meant to find out. It is the method by which we treat as significant what the author did not mean to be significant, by which we single out as essential what the author regarded as incidental. Thus, if one brings out a book on turnips, the modern scholar tries to discover from it whether the author was on good terms with his wife; if a poet writes on buttercups, every word he says may be used as evidence against him at an inquest of his views on a future existence. On this fascinating principle, we delight to extort economic evidence from Aristophanes, because Aristophanes knew nothing of economics; we try to extract cryptograms from Shakespeare, because we are inwardly certain that Shakespeare never put them there; we sift and winnow the Gospel of St Luke, in order to produce a Synoptic problem, because St Luke, poor man, never knew the Synoptic problem to exist.

There is, however, a special fascination in applying this method to Sherlock Holmes, because it is, in a sense, Holmes' own method. 'It has long been an axiom of mine', he says, 'that the little things are infinitely the most important.' It might be the motto of his life's work. And it is, is it not, as we clergymen say, by the little things, the apparently unimportant things, that we judge of a man's character.

If anyone objects that the study of Holmes literature is unworthy of scholarly attention, I might content myself with replying that to the scholarly mind anything is worthy of study, if that study be thorough and systematic. But I will go further, and say that at the present time we need a far closer familiarity with

30

Sherlock's methods. The evil that he did lived after him, the good is interred with him in the Reichenbach. It is a known fact, that is, that several people contracted the dirty and deleterious habit of taking cocaine as a result of reading the books. It is equally obvious that Scotland Yard has benefited not a whit either by his satire or by his example. When Holmes, in *The Mystery of the Red-Headed League*, discovered that certain criminals were burrowing their way into the cellars of a bank, he sat with a dark lantern in the cellar, and nabbed them quietly as they came through. But when the Houndsditch gang were found to be meditating an exactly similar design, what did the police authorities do? They sent a small detachment of constables, who battered on the door of the scene of operations at the bank, shouting, 'We think there is a burglary going on in here.' They were of course shot down, and the Home Office had to call out a whole regiment with guns and a fire brigade, in order to hunt down the survivors.

Any studies in Sherlock Holmes must be, first and foremost, studies in Dr Watson. Let us treat at once of the literary and bibliographical aspect of the question. First, as to authenticity. There are several grave inconsistencies in the Holmes cycle. For example *A Study in Scarlet* and the *Reminiscences* are from the hand of John H. Watson, MD, but in the story of *The Man with the Twisted Lip*, Mrs Watson addresses her husband as James. The present writer, together with three brothers, wrote to ask Sir Arthur Conan Doyle for an explanation, appending their names in the proper style with crosses after them, and an indication that this was the sign of the Four. The answer was that it was an error, an error, in fact, of editing. 'Nihil aliud hic latet,' says the great Sauwosch, 'nisi redactor ignorantissimus.' Yet this error gave the original impetus to Backnecke's theory of the Deutero-Watson, to whom he assigns *A Study in Scarlet*, *The Gloria Scott*, and *The Return of Sherlock Holmes*. He leaves to the proto-Watson the rest of the *Memoirs*, the *Adventures*, *The Sign of Four* and *The Hound of the Baskervilles*. He disputed *A Study in Scarlet* on other grounds, the statement in it, for example, that Holmes' knowledge of literature and philosophy was nil, where it is clear that the true Holmes was a man of wide reading and deep thought. We shall deal with this in its proper place.

The Gloria Scott is condemned by Backnecke partly on the

ground of the statement that Holmes was only up for two years at College, while he speaks in *The Musgrave Ritual* of 'my last years' at the university; which Backnecke supposes to prove that the two stories do not come from the same hand. *The Gloria Scott* further represents Victor Trevor's bull-dog as having bitten Holmes on his way down to Chapel, which is clearly untrue, since dogs are not allowed within the gates at either university. 'The bull-dog is more at home', he adds, 'on the Chapel steps, than this fraudulent imitation among the divine products of the Watsons-genius.' A further objection to *The Gloria Scott* is that it exhibits only four divisions out of the eleven-fold division (to be mentioned later) of the complete Holmes-episode, a lower percentage than is found in any other genuine story. For myself, however, I am content to believe that this irregularity is due merely to the exceptional character of the investigation, while the two inaccuracies are too slight (*me judice*) to form the basis for so elaborate a theory. I would include both *The Gloria Scott* and *A Study in Scarlet* as genuine incidents of Holmes-biography.

When we come to *The Final Problem*, the alleged death of Holmes, and his subsequent return in an unimpaired and even vigorous condition, the problem grows darker. Some critics, accepting the *Return* stories as genuine, regard *The Final Problem* as an incident faked by Watson for his own purposes; thus M. Piff-Pouff represents it as an old dodge of the thaumaturgist, and quotes the example of Salmoxis or Gebeleizis among the Getae, who hid underground for two years, and then returned to preach the doctrine of immortality. In fact, M. Piff-Pouff's verdict is thus expressed: 'Sherlockholmes has not at all fallen from the Reichenbach, it is Vatson who has fallen from the pinnacle of his mendacity.' In a similar vein, Bilgemann asserts that the episode is a weak imitation of Empedocles on Etna, the alpenstock being left behind to represent the famous slipper which was revomited by the volcano. 'The episode of *The Final Problem*', in his own immortal language, 'has the Watsons-applecart completely overturned.'

Others, Backnecke of course among them, regard *The Final Problem* as genuine, and the *Return* stories as a fabrication. The evidence against these stories may be divided into (a) those suggested by changes in the character and methods of Holmes,

Oxford Street (or, as it was then known, Regent Circus) in 1888,
looking west. The partners must often have strolled along the
street on their journeys to the West End.

The Lyceum Theatre, Wellington Street, Strand, at night. In *The Sign of Four* Holmes and Watson accompanied Mary Morstan to the portico of the theatre where she had an assignment 'at the third pillar from the left'.

(b) those resting on impossibilities in the narrative itself, (c) inconsistencies found by comparison with the previous narrative.

(a) The true Holmes is never discourteous to a client: the Holmes of *The Adventure of the Three Students* 'shrugged his shoulders in ungracious acquiescence while our visitor ... poured forth his story'. On the other hand, the true Holmes has no morbid craving for serious crime; but when John Hector Macfarlane talks of the probability of being arrested, the detective is represented as saying 'Arrest you! this is most grati— most interesting.' Twice in the *Return* he gibes at his prisoner, a habit from which the true Holmes, whether from professional etiquette or for other reasons, invariably abstains. Again, the false Holmes actually calls a client by her Christian name, an impossible thing to an author whose views had not been distorted by the erroneous presentation of him in the play. He deliberately abstains from food while at work: the real Holmes only does so through absent-mindedness, as in *The Case of the Five Orange Pips*. He quotes Shakespeare in these stories alone, and that three times, without acknowledgment. He gives way to ludicrously bad logic in *The Dancing Men*. He sends Watson as his emissary in *The Solitary Cyclist*, and this is elsewhere unparalleled, for in *The Hound of the Baskervilles* he himself goes down to Dartmoor as well, to watch the case incognito. The true Holmes never splits an infinitive; the Holmes of the *Return* stories splits at least three.

(b) Is it likely that a university scholarship paper—nay, an Oxford scholarship paper, for the quadrangle is mentioned in connection with it—should be printed only one day before the examination? That it should consist of only half a chapter of Thucydides? That this half-chapter should take the examiner an hour and a half to correct for the press? That the proofs of the half-chapter should be in three consecutive slips? Moreover, if a pencil was marked with the name JOHANN FABER, how could the two letters NN, and these two only, be left on the stump? Professor J. A. Smith has further pointed out that it would be impossible to find out from the superimposition of the tracks of front and back bicycle tyres, whether the cyclist was going or coming.

(c) As to actual inconsistencies. In the mystery of *The Solitary Cyclist* a marriage is performed with no one present except the happy couple and the officiating clergyman. In *A Scandal in Bohemia* Holmes, disguised as a loafer, is deliberately called in to give away an unknown bride on the ground that the marriage will not be valid without a witness. In *The Final Problem*, the police secure 'the whole gang with the exception of Moriarty'. In *The Story of the Empty House* we hear that they failed to incriminate Colonel Moran. Professor Moriarty, in the *Return*, is called Professor James Moriarty, whereas we know from *The Final Problem* that James was really the name of his military brother, who survived him. And, worst of all, the dummy in the Baker Street window is draped in '*the old mouse-coloured dressing-gown*'! As if we had forgotten that it was in a *blue* dressing-gown that Holmes smoked an ounce of shag tobacco at a sitting, while he unravelled the dark complication of *The Man with the Twisted Lip!* The detective, says M. Papier Mâché, has become a chameleon. 'This is not the first time', says the more ponderous Sauwosch, 'that a coat of many colours has been as a deception used! But in truth Sherlock, our modern Joseph, has altogether disappeared, and the evil beast Watson has him devoured.'

To this criticism I assent: I cannot assent, however, to the theory of the deutero-Watson. I believe that all the stories were written by Watson, but whereas the genuine cycle actually happened, the spurious adventures are the lucubrations of his own unaided invention. Surely we may reconstruct the facts thus. Watson has been a bit of a gad-about. He is a spendthrift: so much we know from the beginning of *A Study in Scarlet*. His brother, as Holmes finds out by examining the scratches on the keyhole of his watch, was a confirmed drunkard. He himself, as a bachelor, haunts the Criterion Bar: in *The Sign of Four* he admits having had too much Beaune for lunch, behaves strangely at lunch, speaks of firing off a double-barrelled tiger-cub at a musket, and cautions his future wife against taking more than two drops of castor-oil, while recommending strychnine in large doses as a sedative. What happens? His Elijah is taken away from him: his wife, as we know, dies: he slips back into the grip of his old enemy; his practice, already diminished by continued neglect, vanishes away; he is forced to earn a livelihood by patching together clumsy travesties of the wonderful incidents of which he was once the faithful recorder.

Sauwosch has even worked out an elaborate table of his debts to other authors, and to the earlier stories. Holmes' stay in Tibet with the Grand Lama is due to Dr Nikola; the cipher of *The Dancing Men* is read in the same manner as that in *The Gold Bug*, by Edgar Allan Poe; *The Adventure of Charles Augustus Milverton* shows the influence of Raffles. *The Norwood Builder* owes much to *A Scandal in Bohemia*; *The Solitary Cyclist* has the plot of *The Greek Interpreter*; *The Six Napoleons* of *The Blue Carbuncle*; *The Adventure of the Second Stain* is a doublet of *The Naval Treaty*, and so on.

We now pass on to the dating of the various pieces, so far as it can be determined by internal evidence, implicit or explicit. The results may be tabulated thus:

1. *The Gloria Scott*—Holmes' first case.
2. *The Musgrave Ritual*—his second.
3. *A Study in Scarlet*—Watson first appears, i.e. the first of the We-Stories. Date 1879.
4. 1883, *The Speckled Band*.
5. 1887, April, *The Reigate Squires*.
6. Same year, *The Five Orange Pips*.
7. 1888. *The Sign of Four*—Watson becomes engaged.
8. *The Noble Bachelor*. Then comes Watson's marriage, followed closely by
9. *The Crooked Man*.
10. *A Scandal in Bohemia*, and
11. *The Naval Treaty*, apparently in that order.

To some period in the year '88 we must assign 12, 13 and 14, that is, *The Stockbroker's Clerk*, *The Case of Identity*, and *The Red-Headed League*. In the June of '89 we have (15) *The Man with the Twisted Lip*, (16) *The Engineer's Thumb* (summer), and (17) *The Blue Carbuncle* (somewhere in the octave of Christmas). *The Final Problem* is dated '91. Of the remainder, *Silver Blaze*, *The Yellow Face*, *The Resident Patient*, *The Greek Interpreter*, *The Beryl Coronet*, and *The Copper Beeches* are apparently before Watson's marriage, *The Boscombe Valley Mystery* after it: otherwise they are undated.

There remains only *The Hound of the Baskervilles*. This is explicitly dated 1889, that is, it does not pretend to be after the *Return*. Sauwosch, who believes it to be spurious, points out that *The Times* would never have had a leader on Free Trade till after 1903. But this argument from internal evidence defeats itself: we can show by a method somewhat akin to that of Blunt's *Undesigned Coincidences in Holy Scriptures* that it was meant to be before 1901. The old crank who wants to have a lawsuit against the police says it will be known as the case of Frankland versus REGINA—King Edward, as we all know, succeeded in 1901.

I must not waste time over other evidences (very unsatisfactory) which have been adduced to show the spuriousness of *The Hound of the Baskervilles*. Holmes' 'cat-like love of personal cleanliness' is not really inconsistent with the statement in *A Study in Scarlet* that he had pinpricks all over his hand covered with plaster—though this is also used by Backnecke to tell against the genuineness of the earlier production. A more serious question is that of Watson's breakfast-hour. Both in *A Study in Scarlet* and in *The Adventures* we hear that Watson breakfasted after Holmes: in the *Hound* we are told that Holmes breakfasted late. But then, the true inference from this is that Watson breakfasted very late indeed.

Taking, then, as the basis of our study, the three long stories, *The Sign of Four*, *A Study in Scarlet*, and *The Hound of the Baskervilles*, together with the twenty-three short stories, twelve in the *Adventures*, and eleven in the *Memoirs*, we may proceed to examine the construction and the literary antecedents of this form of art. The actual scheme of each should consist, according to the German scholar, Ratzegger, followed by most of his successors, of eleven distinct parts; the order of them may in some cases be changed about, and more or less of them may appear as the story is closer to or further from the ideal type. Only *A Study in Scarlet* exhibits all the eleven; *The Sign of Four* and *Silver Blaze* have ten, *The Boscombe Valley Mystery* and *The Beryl Coronet* nine, *The Hound of the Baskervilles*, *The Speckled Band*, *The Reigate Squires*, and *The Naval Treaty* eight, and so on till we reach *The Five Orange Pips*, *The Crooked Man*, and *The Final Problem* with five, and *The Gloria Scott* with only four.

The first part is the Prooimion, a homely Baker Street scene, with invaluable personal touches, and sometimes a demonstration by the detective. Then follows the first explanation, or Exegesis kata ton diokonta, that is, the client's statement of the case, followed by the Ichneusis, or personal investigation, often including the famous floor-walk on hands and knees. No. 1 is invariable, Nos. 2 and 3 almost always present. Nos. 4, 5 and 6 are less necessary: they include the Anaskeue, or refutation on its own merits of the official theory of Scotland Yard, the first Promenusis (exoterike) which gives a few stray hints to the police, which they never adopt, and the second Promenusis (esoterike), which adumbrates the true course of the investigation to Watson alone. This is sometimes wrong, as in *The Yellow Face.* No. 7 is the Exetasis, or further following up of the trail, including the cross-questioning of relatives, dependants, etc., of the corpse (if there is one), visits to the Record Office, and various investigations in an assumed character. No. 8 is the Anagnorisis, in which the criminal is caught or exposed, No. 9 the second Exegesis (kata ton pheugonta), that is to say the criminal's confession, No. 10 the Metamenusis, in which Holmes describes what his clues were and how he followed them, and No. 11 the Epilogos, sometimes comprised in a single sentence. This conclusion is, like the Prooimion, invariable, and often contains a gnome or quotation from some standard author.

Although *A Study in Scarlet* is in a certain sense the type and ideal of a Holmes story, it is also to some extent a primitive type, of which elements were later discarded. The Exegesis kata ton pheugonta is told for the most part, not in the words of the criminal, but as a separate story in the mouth of the narrator; it also occupies a disproportionate amount of the total space. This shows directly the influence of Gaboriau: his *Detective's Dilemma* is one volume, containing an account of the tracing of the crime back to its author, who is of course a duke: the second volume, *The Detective's Triumph*, is almost entirely a retailing of the duke's family history, dating back to the Revolution, and we only rejoin Lecoq, the detective, in the last chapter. Of course, this method of telling the story was found long and cumbrous, but the French school has not yet seen through it, since *The Mystery of the Yellow Room* leaves a whole unexplained problem to provide copy for *The Perfume of the Lady in Black*.

But the literary affinities of Dr Watson's masterly style are to be looked for further afield than Gaboriau, or Poe, or Wilkie Collins. M. Piff-Pouff especially, in his *Psychologie de Vatson*, has instituted some very remarkable parallels with *The Dialogues of Plato*, and with the Greek drama. He reminds us of the blustering manner of Thrasymachus when he first breaks into the argument of the Republic, and compares the entry of Athelney Jones: 'Oh, come, now, come! Never be ashamed to own up! But what's all this? Bad business, bad business! Stern facts here, no room for theories,' and so on. And when the detective comes back crestfallen after a few days, wiping his brow with a red handkerchief, we remember how Socrates describes the first time in his life when he ever saw Thrasymachus blushing. The rival theories of Gregson and Lestrade only serve to illustrate the multiformity of error.

But the most important point is the nature of the Scotland Yard criticism. Lecoq has his rival, but the rival is his own superior in the detective force, thwarts his schemes out of pique, and actually connives at the prisoner's receiving notes through the window of his cell. The jealousy of a Lestrade has none of this paltry spirit about it, it is a combination of intellectual pride and professional pique. It is the opposition of the regular force to the amateur. Socrates was hated by the sophists because they took money, and he did not. The cases in which Holmes takes money, explicitly at any rate, are few. In *A Scandal in Bohemia* he is given £1,000, but this would seem to be only for current expenses, and may well have been refunded. At the end, he refuses the gift of an emerald ring. He will not allow the City and Suburban Bank to do more than pay his expenses in connection with The Red-Headed League. He says the same elsewhere: 'As for my reward, my profession is my reward.' On the other hand, he takes £4,000 from Mr Holder when he has recovered the missing beryls for £3,000. In *A Study in Scarlet*, when setting out in business, he says: 'I listen to their story, they listen to my comments, and then I pocket my fee.' In *The Greek Interpreter* he affirms that detection is a means of livelihood with him. And in *The Final Problem* we hear that he has been so well paid for his services in several instances to crowned heads that he is thinking of retiring from business and taking to chemistry. We must suppose, therefore, that he did sometimes take payment, but perhaps only where his clients could well afford it. None the less, as compared with the officials, he is a freelance: he has no axe to grind, no promotion to seek. And further, there is an antithesis of method. Holmes is determined not to be led away by side issues and apparent pressure of facts: this it is that raises him above the level of the sophists.

If the sophists have been borrowed from the Platonic dialogue, one element at least has been borrowed from the Greek drama. Gaboriau has no Watson. The confidant of Lecoq is an old soldier, preternaturally stupid, inconceivably inefficient. Watson provides what the Holmes drama needs—a Chorus. He represents the solid, orthodox, respectable view of the world in general; his drabness is accentuated by contrast with the limelight which beats upon the central figure. He remains stable amid the eddy and flux of circumstance.

> Ille bonis faveatque, et consilietur amicis,
> Et regat iratos, et amet peccare timentes:
> Ille dapes laudet mensae brevis, ille salubrem
> Justitiam, legesque, et apertis otia portis.
> Ille tegat commissa, deosque precetur et oret
> Ut redeat miseris, abeat fortuna superbis.

It is to Professor Sabaglione that we owe the profoundest study of Watson in this his choric character. He compares such passages as that in *The Speckled Band*:

Holmes: 'The lady could not move her bed. It must always be in the same relative position to the ventilator and the rope—for such we may call it, since it was clearly never meant for a bell-pull.'
Watson: 'Holmes, I seem to see what you are hinting at. We are only just in time to prevent some subtle and horrible crime.'

with the well-known passage in the Agamemnon,

Cassandra: 'Ah, ah, keep away the bull from the cow! She takes him, the black-horned one, in a net by her device, and smites him; he falls in a watery vessel—I speak to thee of the Mystery of the Treacherous Cauldron.'
Chorus: 'Far be it from me to boast of any particular skill in oracles, but I deduce from these words some impending evil.'

Watson, like the Chorus, is ever in touch with the main action, and seems to share the full privileges of the audience; yet, like the Chorus, he is always about three stages behind the audience in the unravelling of the plot.

And the seal, and symbol, and secret of Watson is, of course, his bowler. It is not like other bowlers: it is a priestly vestment, an *insigne* of office. Holmes may wear a squash hat, but Watson cleaves to his bowler, even at midnight in the silence of Dartmoor, or on the solitary slopes of the Reichenbach. He wears it constantly, even as the archimandrite or the rabbi wears his hat: to remove it would be akin to the shearing of Samson's locks by Delilah. 'Watson and his bowler,' says M. Piff-Pouff, 'they are separable only in thought.' It is his apex of wool, his petasus of invisibility, his *mitra pretiosa*, his triple tiara, his halo. The bowler stands for all that is immutable and irrefragable, for law and justice, for the established order of things, for the rights of humanity, for the triumph of the man over the brute. It towers colossal over sordidness and misery and crime: it shames and heals and hallows. The curve of its brim is the curve of perfect symmetry, the rotundity of its crown is the rotundity of the world. 'From the hats of Holmes' clients,' writes Professor Sabaglione, 'deduce themselves the traits, the habits, the idiosyncrasies: from the hat of Guatson deduces itself his character.' Watson is everything to Holmes—his medical adviser, his foil, his philosopher, his confidant, his sympathizer, his biographer, his domestic chaplain, but above all things else he stands exalted in history as the wearer of the unconquerable bowler hat.

And if the rival detectives are the sophists, and Watson is the Chorus, what of the clients, and what of the criminals? It is most important to remember that these are only secondary figures. 'The murderers of the Holmes cycle,' M. Papier Mâché assures us, 'are of no more importance than the murderers are not in Macbeth.' Holmes himself often deprecates Watson's habit of making the stories too sensational, but he does him an injustice. The authors of crime are not, in Watson, of personal interest, like the Duke in Gaboriau; they have no relation to the detective other than that which subsists between the sleuth-hound and its quarry—the author of *The Mystery of the Yellow Room* was a bungler when he made Jacques Rouletabille the criminal's natural son—they are not animated by lofty or religious motives like the high-flown villains in Mr Chesterton's *Innocence of Father Brown*. All clients are model clients: they state their case in flawless journalese; all criminals are model criminals: they do the cleverest thing a criminal could possibly do

40

in the given circumstances. By a sort of Socratic paradox, we might say that the best detective can only catch the best thief. A single blunder on the part of the guilty man would have thrown all Holmes' deductions out of joint. Love and money are their only incentives: brutality and cunning their indefeasible qualities.

And thus we arrive at the central figure himself, and must try to gather together a few threads in the complex and many-sided character. There is an irony in the process, for Holmes liked to look upon himself as a machine, an inhuman and undifferentiated sleuth-hound. 'L'homme, c'est rien; l'œuvre, c'est tout,' was one of his favourite quotations.

Sherlock Holmes was descended from a long line of country squires: his grandmother was the sister of a French artist: his elder brother Mycroft was, as we all know, more gifted than himself, but found an occupation, if the *Reminiscences* are to be trusted, in a confidential audit of Government accounts. Of Sherlock's school career we know nothing; Watson was at school, and one of his schoolmates was the nephew of a peer, but this seems to have been exceptional there, since it was considered good fun to 'chevy him about the playground and hit him over the shins with a wicket'. This seems to dispose of the idea that Watson was an Etonian. On the other hand, we have no evidence as to his university career, except the testimony (always doubtful) of one of the *Return* stories that he was unacquainted with the scenery of Cambridgeshire. Of Holmes' student days our knowledge is much fuller: he was reserved by nature, and his recreations—boxing and fencing—did not make him many acquaintances. One of his friends was Victor Trevor, son of an ex-convict, who had made his money in the Australian goldfields; another Reginald Musgrave, whose ancestors went back to the Conquest—quite the last word in aristocracy. He lived in a college, but what college? And at which university? The argument that his scientific bent would have naturally taken him to Cambridge defeats itself: for why should he have been only up two years if he wanted a proper scientific training? More and more as I consider the wealth of his two friends, the exclusive aristocracy of the one, and the doggy tendencies of the other, together with the isolation which put even so brilliant a light as Holmes' under a bushel—more and more I incline to the opinion that he was up at the House. But we have no sure evidence.

If he was an Oxford man, he was not a Greats' man. Yet when Watson describes his first impressions of the man at the beginning of *A Study in Scarlet*—the *locus classicus* for Holmes' characteristics—he wrongs him in saying that his knowledge of philosophy is nil, and his knowledge of literature nil. The fact is, clearly, that Holmes did not let his talents appear till he had been living with Watson for some time, and had come to recognize his sterling qualities. In fact, he compares Hafiz with Horace, quotes Tacitus, Jean Paul, Flaubert, Goethe, and Thoreau, and reads Petrarch in a GWR carriage. He has no definite interest in philosophy as such, yet he holds certain definite views on scientific method. A philosopher could not have said, 'when you have eliminated the impossible, whatever remains, however improbable, must be the truth'. He could not have confused observation with inference, as Holmes does when he says: 'Observation shows me you have been to the Post Office' judging by the mud on Watson's boots. There must be inference here, though it may be called implicit inference, however rapid be the transition of thought. Yet Holmes was no Sensationalist. What sublimer confession of faith could any realist make than the remark in *A Study in Scarlet*: 'I ought to know by this time that when a fact appears to be opposed to a long train of deductions, it invariably proves to be capable of bearing some other interpretation'?

And here I must say a word on the so-called 'method of deduction'. M. Papier Mâché has boldly asserted that it was stolen from Gaboriau. M. Piff-Pouff in his well-known article, 'Qu'est-ce que c'est que la déduction?' declares roundly that Holmes' methods were inductive. The two fallacies rests on a common ground. Lecoq has observation: he notices footsteps on the snow. He has powers of inference, for he can infer from such footsteps the behaviour of those who have left them. He has not the method of deduction—he never sits down and reasons out what it is probable the man would have done next. Lecoq has his lens and his forceps: he has not the dressing-gown and the pipe. That is why he had to depend on mere chance, again and again, for picking up lost threads. Holmes no more depended on a chance than he prayed for a miracle. That is why Lecoq, baffled after a long investigation, has to have recourse to a sort of arm-chair detective, who, without leaving the arm-chair, tells him exactly what must have happened. It is wrong to call this latter character, as M. Papier Mâché does, the original of Mycroft: he is the original, if you will, of Sherlock. Lecoq is but the Stanley Hopkins, almost the Lestrade, of his period. Holmes himself has explained for us the difference between observation (or inference) and deduction. It is by observation *a posteriori* that he recognizes Watson's visit to the Post Office from the mud on his trousers; it is by deduction *a priori* that he knows he has been sending a telegram, since he has seen plenty of stamps and post-cards in Watson's desk.

Let us now take two pictures of Sherlock Holmes, the one at leisure, the other at work. Leisure was, of course, abhorrent to him—more so than to Watson. Watson says he was reckoned fleet of foot, but we have only his own word for it, and Holmes always beat him; beyond this alleged prowess we have no evidence of Watson's athleticism, except that he could throw a rocket through a first-floor window. But Holmes had been a boxer and a fencer; during periods of enforced inactivity he fired a revolver at the opposite wall till he had 'marked it with the patriotic device VR'. Violin playing occupied leisure moments when Watson first knew him, but later it seems to be nothing more than a relaxation after hard work. And—this is very important—in this music was the exact antithesis of cocaine. We never hear of the drug being used in order to stimulate the mental faculties for hard work. All the stimulus needed he derived from tobacco. We all know, of course, that he smoked shag; few people could say off-hand what his pipe was made of. As a matter of fact, his tastes were various. The long vigil in Neville St Clair's house was solaced by a briar—this is when he is hard at work; when he sees his way through a problem by inspection, as in *The Case of Identity*, he takes down 'the old and oily clay pipe, which was to him as a counsellor'. In *The Copper Beeches* he takes down 'the long cherrywood pipe with which he was wont to replace his clay when he was in a disputatious rather than a meditative mood'. On one occasion he offers Watson snuff. Watson, by the way, smoked Ship's tobacco when he went into lodgings with Holmes, but must have replaced it soon after with a sterner stuff, thinly veiled under the *nom de plume* of Arcadia Mixture. This expensive product he did not abandon even under the exigencies of married life; though his circumstances were not those of affluence, since he had linoleum laid down in the front hall. But the pipe is not to Watson what it is to Holmes: to Holmes belongs the immortal phrase: 'This will be a three-pipe problem.' He is one of the world's great smokers.

Now let us see Holmes at work. We all know how brisk he becomes at the appearance of a client; how, according to the inimitable phrase in the *Reminiscences*: 'Holmes sat up in his chair and took his pipe out of his mouth, like a hound that has heard the View Halloo.' We have seen him in the mind's eye prowling round the room with his nose an inch from the ground, on the look-out for cigarette-ends, orange-peel, false teeth, domes of silence, and what not, that may have been left behind by the criminal. 'It is not a man,' says M. Binsk, the great Polish critic, 'it is either a beast or a god.'

It is this charge of inhumanity brought against Holmes that I wish specially to rebut. True, he is reported to have been found beating the dead subjects in the laboratory, to see whether or no bruises could be produced after death. True, he was a scientist. True, we get passages like that in *The Sign of Four*:

Miss Morstan: from that day to this no word has been heard of my unfortunate father. He came home with his heart full of hope, to find some peace, some comfort, and instead—

She put her hand to her throat, and a choking sob cut short her utterance. 'The date?' asked Holmes, opening his notebook.

But is it true to say that Holmes' anxiety to catch the criminal was not, like Watson's, due to a passion for justice, but to a purely scientific interest in deduction? Such truths are never more than half-truths: it would be hard to say that the footballer plays only for the goal, or that he plays only for the sake of exercise. Humanity and science in Holmes are strangely blended. At one moment we find him saying 'Women are never to be trusted, not even the best of them' (the coward!) or asserting that he cannot agree with those who rank modesty among the virtues, since the logician must see all things exactly as they are. Even his little sermon on the rose in *The Naval*

Treaty is delivered in order to cover the fact that he is examining the window-frame for scratches. At another moment he is purchasing 'something a little choice in white wines', and discoursing on miracle plays, on Stradivarius violins, on the Buddhism of Ceylon, and on the warships of the future.

But there are two specially human characteristics which come out at the very moment of action. One is a taste for theatrical arrangement, as when he sends back five orange pips to the murderers of John Openshaw, or takes a sponge into prison with which to unmask the man with the twisted lip, or serves up the Naval Treaty under a cover as a breakfast dish. The other is a taste for epigram. When he gets a letter from a duke, he says: 'It looks like one of those social summonses which call upon a man either to be bored or to lie.' There is a special kind of epigram, known as the Sherlockismus, of which the indefatigable Ratzegger has collected no less than 173 instances. The following may serve as examples:

> 'Let me call your attention to the curious incident of the dog in the night-time.'
> 'The dog did nothing at all in the night-time.'
> 'That was the curious incident,' said Sherlock Holmes—

and again:

> 'I was following you, of course.'
> 'Following me? I saw nobody.'
> 'That is what you must expect to see when I am following you,' said Sherlock Holmes.

To write fully on this subject would need two terms' lectures at least. Some time, when leisure and enterprise allow, I hope to deliver them. Meanwhile, I have thrown out these hints, drawn these outlines of a possible mode of treatment. You know my methods, Watson: apply them.

$$\Rightarrow \ast \; 4 \; \ast \Leftarrow$$

S. C. ROBERTS

THE CHRONOLOGICAL PROBLEM

The recent publication (1928) of *The Complete Sherlock Holmes Short Stories* and of *Essays in Satire* by R. A. Knox (Sheed and Ward) offers a convenient opportunity for a brief commentary on the thesis presented in the latter volume by the learned Knocksius and entitled *Studies in the Literature of Sherlock Holmes*.

Knocksius' brilliant, if somewhat superficial, survey of the work of his predecessors in this field (Backnecke, Sauwosch, Piff-Pouff, Papier Mâché, and Ratzegger) undoubtedly has its merits as a *prolegomenon* to the study of *das Watsonischechronologieproblem*, but it is a matter for some surprise that this article, first written in 1911, should now be issued unrevised and without reference, even by way of a footnote, to the investigations of later scholarship. There is no mention, for instance, of the interesting, though not wholly convincing, theory put forward by Rendallus in 1917 to account for the solecisms inherent in *The Three Students* (*The London Nights of Belsize*).

More serious, however, are the flagrant inaccuracies in the chronological tabulation of the *Adventures and Memoirs* as prepared by Knocksius (*Essays in Satire*, pp. 155, 156) and based on 'internal evidence, implicit or explicit'. Let us examine one or two examples of Knocksius' reckless handling of this evidence:

1. He writes:

'To some period in the year '88 we must assign . . . *The Stockbroker's Clerk* . . . and *The Red-Headed League*.'

There is little occasion for speculation in the matter of the date of either of these adventures, since in the second paragraph of *The Stockbroker's Clerk* Watson states explicitly that Holmes called on him *one morning in June, as he sat reading the British*

Medical Journal. About the date of *The Red-Headed League*, Watson is even more explicit: the advertisement of a vacancy in the League appeared in the *Morning Chronicle* of April 27, 1890, and the notice of its dissolution on October 9, 1890. So much for Knocksius' 'some period in the year '88'.

2. Knocksius places *The Blue Carbuncle*, with a kind of ecclesiastical vagueness, 'somewhere in the octave of Christmas'. This is less serious, but in the interests of accurate scholarship, should not be passed without comment. Watson records in the first sentence that he called upon his friend *upon the second morning after Christmas*.

3. *The Copper Beeches*, according to Knocksius, is 'apparently before Watson's marriage'. We could wish that Knocksius were less fond of the word 'apparently'. What is apparent to us is that in the course of this adventure Holmes refers to the Man with the Twisted Lip (June 1889—the year after Watson's marriage) as past history.

In justice to Knocksius it is only fair to say that the whole problem bristles with difficulties. Neither Keibosch nor Pauvremütte seems to us to have faced the central problem—the date of Watson's marriage. To review the whole evidence would be out of place here, but one or two of the major difficulties may be indicated in the interests of future research:

1. Watson became engaged in 1888 (*The Sign of Four*).

2. *The Crooked Man* is dated 'a few months after', and *The Naval Treaty* is assigned to 'the July which immediately succeeded' the marriage; but

3. *A Scandal in Bohemia*, which is categorically dated March 20, 1888, occurs after marriage 'had drifted us [Watson and Holmes] away from each other'. The length, or width, of this drift is not specified, but in the course of it Holmes had been engaged on a successful mission on behalf of the Dutch royal house and had travelled to Odessa and back in connection with the Trepoff murder. Watson had only heard of these things through the daily papers.

Knocksius places *A Scandal in Bohemia* between *The Crooked Man* and *The Naval Treaty*; the three adventures are to be dated, he says, 'apparently in that order'—on what grounds we have been unable to determine.

Knocksius' incursions into critical exegesis are not wholly

fortunate. Following Backnecke in his attack upon the authenticity of the *Return* stories he writes:

> In *The Story of the Empty House* . . . the dummy . . . is draped in '*the old mouse-coloured dressing gown*'! As if we had forgotten that it was in a *blue* dressing-gown that Holmes smoked an ounce of shag tobacco at a sitting, while he unravelled the dark complications of *The Man with the Twisted Lip*!

This is sound enough, so far as it goes; but it is to be feared that Knocksius has forgotten that it was in a *purple* dressing-gown that Holmes reclined upon the sofa when he tackled the problem of *The Blue Carbuncle*! Further, *The Blue Carbuncle* belongs to the *Adventures*, not to the *Return* series. Knocksius must at least abandon the shade of Holmes' dressing-gown as a test of canonicity.

We should read Knocksius' purely literary criticism with greater enjoyment if our confidence in his scholarship were not shaken by the fear that his texts are not wholly above suspicion. In his illustrations, for instance, of the highly important figure known to students as the *Sherlockismus* he quotes two passages. The first is the well-known dialogue from *Silver Blaze*:

> 'Let me call your attention to the curious incident of the dog in the night-time.'
> 'The dog did nothing at all in the night-time.'
> 'That was the curious incident,' said Sherlock Holmes.

It is possible that Knocksius has his own textual authority for what appears to us to be a wholly unwarrantable conflation. We do not claim to have made an entirely exhaustive study of each family of Watson texts, but in such editions as we have been able to consult, the passage runs:

> 'Is there any other point to which you would wish to draw my attention?'
> 'To the curious incident of the dog in the night-time.'
> 'The dog did nothing in the night-time.'
> 'That was the curious incident,' remarked Sherlock Holmes.

The interpolation of the superfluous *at all* and the substitution of the prosaic *said* for the more picturesque *remarked* do not argue well for a sense either of linguistic accuracy or of euphonious expression.

The second illustration is even more remarkable. No reference is given, but 'apparently' it is taken, without verification, from Ratzegger's notoriously unreliable *Collectanea*; and, unless we are mistaken, it is a quotation, or rather a reckless misquotation, from *The Devil's Foot*, a story which, if Knocksius' hypothesis were accepted, would be excluded from the canon.

The whole problem of the composition of the latest collections (*His Last Bow* and *The Case-Book*) is outside the scope of Knocksius' paper, but one chronological point may be referred to here. In *The Veiled Lodger* it is recorded that Sherlock Holmes was in active practice for twenty-three years. Now, Knocksius ascribes *A Study in Scarlet* to the year 1879. Twenty-three years from that date would bring us to the year 1902; yet *The Creeping Man* is explicitly dated 1903. Furthermore, we know that the battle in which Watson was wounded was fought in July 1880, so that his association with Holmes cannot possibly have begun before the later months of 1880.

Finally, in the *Complete Short Stories* one observes a regrettable laxity in the simple matter of place-names. The adventure in which Holmes made his 'final exit' is described in the preface as 'The Adventure of Shoscombe Abbey', but in the text we find 'Shoscombe Old Place'. Trifles such as these may be of some interest to the amateur of textual collation, but it is to be hoped that serious students will rather devote their energies to the elucidation of the major problems of Watsonian chronology, the complexity of which we have sought but to adumbrate.

⇒ ＊ 5 ＊ ⇐

DESMOND MACCARTHY

DR WATSON

At no other period of literary history have biographers shown such brilliant independence of documents, such ingenuity in surmise. Biographers of an earlier date would never have told us, for instance, that cats were playing in the area, or a milk-cart was passing by when Keats was born, nor did it occur to them to introduce their hero, as it were, *incognito*, a minor figure in the midst of some trivial but brilliantly imagined scene. They, the old biographers, began, you remember, in a different fashion. They opened with a statement of the place and date at which the biographee was born, and with an account of his descent. I cannot bring home to you more directly the drawback of such old-fashioned methods than by saying at once that, if we still adhered to them, it would be almost impossible to write the life of the most representative Englishman of the latter end of the nineteenth century—I mean, of course, Dr Watson, friend and chronicler of Sherlock Holmes.

We do not know precisely the date of his birth, and had not his agitation on hearing a few melancholy facts deduced from his brother's watch betrayed him, we should know little about any single member of his family. Dr Watson, in all things typical of his generation, is in none more unlike our own than in his reluctance to make family skeletons dance in public. Although he has never shown the slightest shyness about being drawn, so that did not his moustache, his clothes and his bowler resemble those of countless other men, we should recognize him in the streets, he has always been exceedingly chary of facts about himself, unless they were pertinent to the 'adventure' in hand. This self-respecting, self-effacing habit proclaims his sound middle-class descent, for, though a proud reserve was once supposed to be a sign of breeding, a flighty and confident exhibitionism has become almost the sole remaining peculiarity of too many aristocrats.

And I may add that both he and his friend also betray that descent in their respectfully romantic, yet self-consciously independent attitude towards people of title. For Dr Watson even a baronet or a coroneted envelope adds to the unenvied glamour of the world. Let me add that here he has my entire sympathy: nothing is so dull as equality; where there is no inequality there is no fun.

Owing to this paucity of direct information, though, as I shall presently suggest, Dr Watson has told us more about himself than he perhaps intended, you will not be surprised to hear that I have elected to open my forthcoming and profusely illustrated biography of him in the modern fashion.

The second Afghan War is on the point of breaking out; the great men of the time pass rapidly across the page, diminished, however, to pigmy size in the perspective of my own powerful and quizzical intellect. At last, upon the crowded deck of a steamer destined for Bombay, the reader is permitted to observe a young straight-backed, strong-backed Army surgeon. He is attached to the Fifth Northumberland Fusiliers, already stationed in India. He has a fair moustache and he is correctly if inexpensively dressed. Although it is his habit to cling to his bowler in roughest parts of rural England he discards it in the Red Sea. His opinions are wholesome and invariably predictable.

This, you perceive, is the new *incognito* method. The reader is gently titillated by his shrewd guess that this young man is no other than *the* Dr Watson, though the young man himself —and I believe this is what the Greeks called irony—is ignorant (not, of course, of the fact), but of its far-flung implications. Though reserved in print there is no reason to suppose that Lieutenant Watson would be otherwise than modestly frank in conversation; and, adopting the modern biographer's privilege of recording conversations which did not take place and embodying in them remarks uttered on other occasions, I shall then have an opportunity of narrating his life up to that date—without pinning myself down to tiresome particularities. He has told us himself that he took his degree of Doctor of Medicine of the University of London in 1878. Well, from evidence it would take too long to marshal, we know he was not brilliant. Indeed, I have always suspected that when Holmes refused, in *The Case of the Dying Detective*, to allow Watson to prescribe for him and told him roundly that he was 'only a general practitioner with very limited experience and mediocre qualifications', the great man was not only acting a part but also speaking his mind. No: Lieutenant Watson would not be 'our Watson' if he had passed his examinations quickly. He would have taken a full five years and more to qualify. If, then, he entered London University at the average age he would be twenty-four when he took his degree, thus we arrive at the date of his birth, 1854. He arrived in India just in time for the battle of Maiwand, which took place in July 1880, so when his biographer first catches sight of him and overhears him he is twenty-six. Highly susceptible, as his courtship of Miss Morstan in *The Sign of Four* shows, honest caution would lead him, though scrupulously polite, to avoid female companionship on board. It would be, then, in the deck smoking-room (minutely described) that he would impart the following facts about himself: that he had only his professional prospects, and 'neither kith nor kin in England'; that his late father had been an unsuccessful man but a conscientious parent who had emigrated to Australia; that his elder brother had been a great cause of anxiety and disappointment; that he himself had spent his childhood in Australia; then been sent to England to a small inexpensive school, where a nephew by marriage of a lord (you remember, of course, 'Tadpole' Phelps in *The Naval Treaty*) was enough of a *rara avis* to attract a certain amount of ironic ragging.

Do you wonder at my temerity in allowing such definite statements to drop from my hero's lips—as the steamer furrows its quiet way across the dark blue circle of the sea? Have no fear, if my reviewers dispute them they will receive a crushing reply.

From Watson himself we learn in *A Study in Scarlet* that his father was dead and that he had no relations in England; observe he did not say that he had none elsewhere. That the family had emigrated to Australia and that it was from Australia the funds just sufficient for his own education arrived, is an easy

deduction from a remark that he makes himself in telling the
story of *The Sign of Four*. You remember in that story that the
sight of the dug-up grounds of Pondicherry Lodge instantly
reminds him of the excavations on the side of a hill in Ballarat.
Now he could not have visited Australia between his return to
England from India and the date of that adventure, for during
all those years he was living in Baker Street with Sherlock
Holmes. It was therefore a recollection of childhood—of the
years which preceded his school days with 'Tadpole' Phelps—
which prompted the comparison. I just give this example to
show that though my methods as a biographer may be modern,
my conscience is that of the old-fashioned historian.

I will not trouble you with his rush to Afghanistan, nor with
the battle of Maiwand and the subsequent relief of Kandahar
by Lord Roberts' gallant march, though such incidents supply
some of my brightest pages. It was at that disastrous engagement, to use Dr Watson's own words, that he was 'struck on the
shoulder by a Jezail bullet which shattered the bone and grazed
the sub-clavian artery'. He was 'removed to the base hospital
at Peshawar', where he was healed of his wound, but caught
enteric fever. I say healed, although—and this is an unexpected
fact which a biographer must blindly accept—he limped for
years afterwards, and in damp weather, as you well remember,
was always apt to feel pain in his leg. He was invalided home on
the troopship *Orontes* and he landed at Portsmouth towards the
end of December 1880.

There was a dash of wild blood in the Watsons. We know
from his elder brother's watch that he died prematurely from
drink and in poverty, in spite of excellent abilities which enabled
him intermittently to retrieve his position in the world. The
first month or so of Watson's life after his return to England
was a period to which he looked back with misgivings. The
modern tendency in biography to emphasize the regrettable side
of human nature may tempt to read more than is justifiable into
that violent phrase which Watson employs in describing London—he speaks of it as 'that great cesspool into which all the
loungers and idlers of the Empire are irresistibly drained'—
but there can be little doubt that during the first two months of
1880, for the last time in his life, Watson sowed a few wild oats.
The gods, Shakespeare says in his old-fashioned way, make

scourges of our pleasant vices. It is more in harmony with the tone of modern biography to point out here that had not young Stamford of Bart's clapped Watson on the shoulder as he leant across the Criterion zinc talking to the barmaid, the latter would never have met Holmes.

As everyone knows, it was economy that first compelled the two friends to keep house together. Watson, with what may be called his superb normality, had found it impossible to live independently on his military pension of £209 6s. Economy was equally necessary in the case of the young Sherlock Holmes. We know that Mrs Hudson's charges were extremely moderate, but it seems scarcely possible that with food, light and fuel they could, even in the 'eighties, have been less than £5 a week. We know that Holmes' clientele was at first by no means wealthy, and that his artist's devotion to his profession often induced him to undertake cases which left him out of pocket. However, fame came rapidly, while Watson succeeded in placing his literary work. By 1888 all financial troubles were over.

There is in the records of his life what Henry James would have called a great straddling unaccommodating fact: he appears to have been married in two different years. This has led to the wildest surmises, even to the reckless suggestion that he kept two establishments. Apart from the importance of finding a solution from the point of view of clearing the character of Dr Watson himself, it is necessary to determine the precise year of his marriage if we are to arrange the stories in chronological order, since Dr Watson constantly used his own marriage as a sort of BC or AD in recounting events. It is *The Sign of Four*, of course, which gives us the circumstances which led up to it. What was the date of this adventure? Before discussing this point, which I warn you will require the application of all your arithmetical faculties, let me state what the point at issue is: did Dr Watson marry Miss Morstan in the autumn of 1887 or of 1888? There is evidence for both alternatives. I brush aside as frivolous the suggestion that Watson had two wives. The perfect character of Mrs Watson, who not only never kept him from his old friend, but even encouraged him to jeopardize his practice by continually going off upon 'adventures', are alone sufficient to refute it. Those who make it may be acute reasoners but they know little of matrimony and nothing of bigamy—its cause and cure.

Let us bend our minds for a moment to this question of dates and weigh the evidence. In *A Scandal in Bohemia*, which is expressly stated to have occurred in March 1888, Watson is already married. He was about to be married in a few weeks when the events described in *The Noble Bachelor* took place. And the date of that story is fixed by Holmes' reference to Lord St Simon's age—'Born in 1846, he is forty-one years old'. It is, therefore, the autumn of 1887. This is the case for fixing Watson's marriage in the autumn of that year. Now let us examine the case of those who favour the view that he was married in the autumn of 1888. *The Sign of Four* gives us, as every schoolboy knows, the circumstances which led up to his marriage. When Miss Morstan called at Baker Street with the letter asking her to be at the third pillar from the left outside the Lyceum that night, Holmes asked to see the envelope: 'Postmark, London, S.W. Date, July 7. Hum!' he remarked; the date of her visit was therefore July 8. Nor is the year apparently less certain. 'About six years ago—to be exact, upon the 4th of May, 1882—an advertisement appeared in *The Times* asking for the address of Miss Mary Morstan', she also told him. From her words 'six years ago' many have concluded that *A Sign of Four* must be assigned to 1888.

But those who think so have failed to notice one significant fact. From May 1882, onwards, every year, on the same day Miss Morstan had received 'a very large and lustrous pearl' from an unknown benefactor. If, as she asserted, the first had arrived on May 4, 'six years ago', she would have received by July 7, 1888, seven pearls. Mark that. But the box she showed Dr Watson only contained '*six* of the finest pearls he had ever seen'. Is it not the more reasonable to suppose that Miss Morstan habitually used the words 'about so long ago' a little vaguely (she was clearly fond of using the phrase, for in a short conversation she uses it twice), than that she had lost a pearl and said nothing about her loss? It seems to me far safer to trust the evidence of the pearls themselves than her hasty estimate of the number of years which had passed since she began to receive them, and in that case the otherwise sinister implications deducible from *A Scandal in Bohemia* and *The Noble Bachelor* entirely disappear. There is another reason for not laying too much stress upon the complete verbal accuracy of all statements in *The Sign of Four*. Dr Watson during his short and passionate courtship was thrown into great confusion of mind. Holmes (you remember) declared afterwards that he had overheard him caution the unhappy Sholto against the great danger of taking more than two drops of castor oil while he recommended strychnine in large doses as a sedative. We need not therefore be *very* surprised that Dr Watson in recounting the events of that evening of July 8th should, in writing his account of it afterwards, say 'it was a September evening and a dense drizzly fog lay low upon the great city'. No. A story so evidently written in a hubble-bubble of emotion must not be used, and the reputation of one concerning whom every reader feels that whatever record leaps to light he ought never to be shamed, is saved.

⇒ ✳ 6 ✳ ⇐

DOROTHY L. SAYERS

THE DATES IN
THE RED-HEADED LEAGUE

Among the curious chronological problems encountered by the
Sherlock Holmes student, one of the most delicate and fascinating is that of the dates in *The Red-Headed League*. Its difficulties
have been most ably set forth by Mr H. W. Bell in his scholarly
and comprehensive study, *Sherlock Holmes and Dr Watson*. This
work—the first and only attempt to place *all* the cases in
chronological order—must inevitably form the basis of all
future Holmes-Watson exegesis, and the following statement of
the problem is summarized from its pages:

1. Watson says that Jabez Wilson's visit to Baker Street took
place on a Saturday in the autumn of 1890. Later on, the day
is fixed, by the notice on the door of the League's premises, as
October 9th. But October 9, 1890, was a Thursday.

2. The advertisement shown to Holmes on this occasion is
stated by Watson to have appeared in the *Morning Chronicle* of
April 27th, 'just two months ago'. This is incompatible with
all the other dates.

3. Jabez Wilson says that the advertisement appeared 'this
day eight weeks', which, reckoning back from October 9th,
would bring it to Thursday, August 14th.

4. Wilson also says that the League paid him £4 every
Saturday for eight weeks, and that this 'cost them two-and-
thirty pounds'. It is hardly conceivable that Wilson should be
mistaken about the money he received. But on the last Saturday ('October 9th') the office of the League was closed, and
he got no pay. If, therefore, he only worked for eight weeks, he
should have received only £28 in all.

Let us now see what we can make of these contradictions. The year 1890 is determined by the original date of publication in *The Strand Magazine* for August 1891 ('One day in the autumn of last year') and by the notice on the League door ('The Red-Headed League is dissolved, Oct. 9, 1890'). The day of the week on which Wilson visited Holmes is also fixed, not merely by Holmes' own statements ('today is Saturday'—'today being Saturday rather complicates matters'), but also by the fact that, as Mr Bell points out, 'the choice of Saturday was an essential part of the bank-robbers' plot'. The visit to Baker Street, the investigation at Wilson's establishment, and the final capture of the criminals all take place within twenty-four hours (Saturday morning[1] to the early hours of Sunday), so that we are restricted to a Saturday in the autumn of 1890. Since the date 'April 27th' is an obvious error, which could not by any stretch of the imagination be called 'a day in the autumn', there is no reason to reject the month of October mentioned in the notice. We are therefore obliged to choose between the four Saturdays in October 1890, which fell on the 4th, 11th, 18th and 25th respectively.

Mr Bell, thinking that Dr Watson may have misread his own figure '4' as a '9', selects October 4th. I emphatically agree that this is the correct date, though I differ from Mr Bell as to the precise way in which the mistake came about. In my opinion, the crucial points of the problem are (*a*) the surprising error 'April 27th', and (*b*) the discrepancy about the money, neither of which anomalies is accounted for in Mr Bell's commentary. In the following notes I shall hope to show exactly how (*a*) occurred, and to prove that (*b*) was no error at all, and thus to establish the date by two independent and mutually supporting lines of reasoning.

1. The date October 4th for Wilson's visit to Holmes is *a priori* the most likely, since, as Mr Bell remarks, Watson is hardly likely to have mistaken any one of the double figures 11, 18, or 25 for the single figure 9.

2. The advertisement in the *Morning Chronicle* directed the applicants to attend at 7 Pope's Court 'on Monday'. It was

[1] Mr Bell says 'early afternoon'; but Wilson's visit, Holmes' fifty minutes of reflection, and the journey to the City all took place before lunch. Wilson probably arrived about eleven o'clock, coming immediately from Pope's Court, which he had reached at 10 a.m.

evidently on the very Monday specified in the advertisement that Vincent Spaulding showed the paper to Wilson, since they 'put the shutters up' and started for Pope's Court immediately.

3. The wording of the advertisement at first sight suggests that it appeared in the previous Saturday's issue, and this suggestion is supported by Wilson's remark that it appeared 'this day *eight weeks*'. On examination, however, this will not hold water. If the advertisement appeared on the Saturday, why did Spaulding (who lived on the premises) not show it to Wilson at once? Why should he be reading Saturday's paper on Monday morning? The inference is that the advertisement actually appeared on the Monday. The wording may have been due to carelessness; or the advertisement may have been intended to appear on the Saturday and have been crowded out or arrived too late for insertion on that day.

4. This view is strongly supported by Watson's remark that the advertisement appeared 'just *two months* ago'. This, if accurate, brings us back to Monday, August 4th. Wilson, no doubt, made the common error of reckoning a month as four weeks, whereas Watson was going correctly by the calendar.

5. Duncan Ross asked Wilson if he could 'be ready tomorrow', and he accordingly started work the day following the interview, viz. Tuesday, August 5th. On the Saturday immediately succeeding, he was paid £4 'for my week's work'. Actually, he had only worked five days, but the salary would, no doubt, be reckoned as from the time of his engagement on the Monday, and, in fact, it is clear from the text that this was so.

6. Wilson thus received in all eight payments of £4, viz. on August 9th, 16th, 23rd and 30th, and September 6th, 13th, 20th and 27th, before the League was dissolved on the morning of the *ninth* Saturday, October 4th; these payments making up the correct total of £32.

7. The only difficulties which now remain are the two incorrect dates given in the text: (*a*) April 27th as the date of the advertisement, and (*b*) October 9th as the date of the dissolution of the League.

(*a*) This is patently absurd, and suggests the error of a not-too-intelligent compositor at work upon a crabbed manuscript.

SEVENTEEN STEPS TO 221B

Watson was a doctor, and his writing was therefore probably illegible at the best of times; moreover, he may have written his dates in a contracted form and used, in addition, a J pen in a poor state of repair. The adjoined pair of figures show how easily 'Augst 4' might be mistaken, under these conditions, for 'April 27'. In this way, the very error itself provides independent testimony that August 4th was the actual date of the advertisement, since it is difficult to see how any of the other dates in August (11, 18, 25)[1] could have been mistaken for 27, while the Saturday dates have already been shown to be impossible. But if August 4th was the date of the advertisement, then October 4th must have been the date of Wilson's visit to Holmes; thus the two conclusions are mutually checked and confirmed. No other system of dating accounts *either* for the error 'April 27th' *or* for the £32, whereas the present hypothesis accounts reasonably for *both* and is the only one that will do so.

(*b*) If we accept this explanation of 'April 27th', we are confronted with a slight difficulty about the second error: 'Oct. 9th' for 'Oct. 4th' in the notice pinned on the League door. Could Watson write the figure '4' in two such dissimilar ways that it could be misread, on the one occasion as '27' and on another occasion as '9'? It seems possible that, in this instance, Watson himself carelessly misread the handwriting of Duncan Ross on the notice-card. Ross may have written his '4' in some such form as is shown in Fig. 3, and Watson, hurriedly espying the inscription, either then or later, when he came to compile his story, may have written down what he thought he saw, without troubling to verify the date by the calendar.

It is, in any case, abundantly clear that the good doctor did not at any time carefully revise his proofs, and it may be (as Mr T. S. Blakeney suggests in *Sherlock Holmes: Fact or Fiction?*) that he was especially vague and distrait when writing this story, owing to 'the (presumed) death of Holmes shortly before, which evidently hit Watson hard'. Had he read his proofs with any

---

[1] Any one of these dates would throw the date of the dissolution of the League forward to a double-figure date (October 11th, 18th, 25th), which could not readily be mistaken for a '9'. August 25th is open to the further objection that Watson (as is clearly proved by Mr Bell in an interesting study of *The Sign of Four*) wrote his '5' rather like a '6', without the cross-bar, so that it certainly could not have resembled a '7'.

attention, he could not possibly have passed the blatant absurdity of 'April 27th'.[1]

Having now shown that October 4th and August 4th are almost certainly the correct dates for Wilson's visits to Holmes and to Pope's Court respectively, we find ourselves face to face with a very remarkable corollary—namely, that the Monday on which the advertisement appeared in the *Morning Chronicle*, and on which Wilson entered upon his engagement with the Red-Headed League, was August Bank Holiday. This appears, at a first glance, to be most improbable. However, in Holmes' own words, 'I ought to know by this time that when a fact appears to be opposed to a long train of deductions it invariably proves to be capable of bearing some other interpretation.' And, in fact, when we examine the text in detail, we shall find the strongest corroborative evidence in favour of Bank Holiday.

Let us begin by examining the nature of Jabez Wilson's business and the geography of Saxe-Coburg Square (or Coburg Square; there seems to be some doubt as to the precise title, due also, no doubt, to Watson's slip-shod method of jotting down his notes).

The first thing we observe is that Wilson describes his establishment as 'a small pawnbroker's business'. Now, pawnbroking is usually carried on in connection with a shop of some kind, having a window in which unredeemed pledges are displayed for sale. But there is no mention of either shop or window[2] in connection with Jabez Wilson's pawnbroking, and it is, in fact, quite evident from the text that nothing of the kind existed. On p. 42 Holmes says, 'Today is Saturday', and, after a brief interval of contemplation, turns to Watson with the words, 'Put on your hat and come.' It is before lunch (p. 43), and therefore all the shops would be open, and certainly were open, for we read on p. 44 of 'the immense stream of commerce' and the footpaths 'black with the hurrying swarm of pedestrians'. This was *after*

---

[1] Students may object that Mr Bell has discovered another occasion (*The Man with the Twisted Lip*) on which Watson read his own '4' as a '9' (Bell, p. 66). But I am inclined to think that here Mr Bell's second suggestion may be the correct one, and that Watson simply wrote 'Ju. 19th', forgetting that this abbreviation might stand either for June or for July.

[2] It is true that *The Strand Magazine* artist depicts the establishment with a window which appears to be intended for a shop window, but no goods are displayed there. In any case, the evidence of the illustrations is only to be accepted with caution. See Mr Bell's section on *The Musgrave Ritual* (p. 14).

the visit to Wilson's, so that we may conclude that, if Wilson had had a shop, it should have been open, when Holmes and Watson called.

This being so, if Holmes wanted to see the shop-assistant, Vincent Spaulding, in a casual way, without arousing suspicion, what should we expect him to do? Surely to walk straight in and inquire the price of some object in the window. (True, in such a case, the knees of Spaulding's trousers, which Holmes particularly wanted to examine, might have been concealed by the counter, but that difficulty could readily have been overcome by requesting him to bring the object forward into the light of the doorway.) But it seems clear that no such opportunity presented itself. The place was only 'announced' by 'three gilt balls and a brown board'. There was no shop and no window, and Holmes was thus obliged to fall back upon knocking at the door of the house and, on having it opened to him, putting forward an unconvincing inquiry about the way to the Strand, which could have been put with far more propriety at the tobacconist's, the little newspaper shop or the Vegetarian Restaurant.

So far, so good. There was no shop; and we must suppose that the business was a moneylending business and nothing more, unredeemed pledges being presumably disposed of by private arrangement with other second-hand establishments.

Let us now go back to the events of Monday, August 4th, the day on which Wilson and Spaulding answered the advertisement.

We are told that, on this occasion, Vincent Spaulding 'came down into the office'. This, to begin with, supports the conclusion that the business was carried on in an office and not in a shop. Where, then, did Spaulding come 'down' from? Certainly not from the shop, if such had existed (for any shop or place of public business would be on the ground floor), unless we suppose the 'office' to have been in the basement, which seems scarcely reasonable, If, then, Spaulding came 'down' to the office, it was either from a bedroom or living-room on an upper floor, or else from some upper room used for the storage of goods. If he came from a living-room or (*a fortiori*) from a bedroom, then he was idling while his employer worked, and, with so exceptionally diligent a young man, how could that have happened at any other time than a public holiday? (I shall come presently to the nature of Jabez Wilson's work in the office.) If, on the other hand, Spaulding came 'down' from a store-room, it is quite possible that he was engaged in putting away and inventorying the goods deposited there—a very suitable occupation for a day on which no regular business was being transacted. Actually, I am inclined to think that he was thus employed,[1] since on p. 35 Wilson states that Spaulding 'was very glad to have a holiday', thus suggesting that he would in the ordinary course of events, have expected to work on that particular day.

Jabez Wilson, in the office, was undoubtedly at work—and upon what? It appears very likely that both he and Spaulding were engaged in storing, valuing and otherwise dealing with pledges deposited on the previous Saturday, and booking up the various transactions completed on that day. Thursday and Friday, as we know, were normally Wilson's busiest days, but Saturday, being pay-day, is the day on which pledges are most frequently redeemed, and pawnbrokers always keep open to a late hour on Saturdays. This means that a good deal of business would be left to be carried over, on Monday, from the day-book to the ledger. In addition, if the Monday was a Bank Holiday, there would also be a number of thriftless people who had actually pawned goods on the Saturday so as to get extra money for their week-end pleasuring. Thus we get a mental picture of Spaulding engaged (or supposed to be engaged) in stocktaking upstairs, while his employer is at work on the books in the office, both taking advantage of the public holiday to set their house in order. It is also quite conceivable that they would not be averse from doing a little moneylending even on a Bank Holiday morning. What was there to prevent the man who had squandered his wages in the public-house on the Saturday and Sunday from sending his wife round to knock discreetly at the front door on Monday, bringing the family bible or the flat-irons in a modest paper parcel?

But now we come to a very important point. When Spaulding

[1] At the moment when he came down he was presumed to have been reading the paper, but this need only mean that he had knocked off work for a few minutes. Perhaps it was the regular time for his 'elevenses'. He would not, of course, get the paper till Wilson had finished with it.

had shown Jabez Wilson the paper, he was instructed to 'put up the shutters for the day and come right away'; after which Wilson adds, 'so we shut the business up'. Immediately we ask ourselves: If there was no shop-window, to what shutters does this refer? Why should any shutters be put up at all? If this was an ordinary weekday, with the 'girl of fourteen' at home and working about the house, what imaginable reason could there be for putting up the shutters, which (in the absence of a shop), could only be the shutters of the 'office' or the dwelling rooms? The point is puzzling, in any case; but the most reasonable answer seems to be this: That it was Bank Holiday, that the girl had been given the day off, and that the shutters were put up on the ground floor, first, to indicate to any caller that there was nobody to answer the door and secondly, as a measure of protection for the money in the office safe, which could not, of course, have been paid in to the bank either on the Saturday evening, the Sunday or the Bank Holiday morning. In short, the shutters were put up because the house was empty, and the expression 'we shut the business up' probably merely means that the work upon the books, etc., was discontinued.

The next passage to be considered is the description of the journey to Pope's Court. It is noticeable that no mention is made anywhere of open shops or of the ordinary City traffic. On the contrary, it is distinctly asserted that 'Fleet Street was choked' with red-headed folk, and that Pope's Court was packed 'like a coster's orange-barrow'. This was in 1890, not in 1934. Even today, it would be difficult to find enough permanently unemployed red-headed men in London[1] to 'choke' Fleet Street on a working day; in 1890, it would have been impossible. Therefore, if all these men were able to leave their work to answer an advertisement, it must have been because Bank Holiday had already released them. And can we suppose that so serious a dislocation of the traffic as the 'choking' of Fleet Street would imply could have been permitted on a working day without police interference? Evidently there was no attempt at the formation of an orderly queue outside the League premises, since Spaulding was permitted to 'push, pull and butt' his way through the crowd; yet we hear of no protest from the occupiers

[1] The advertisement had only appeared that morning, and there was no time for applicants to come in from the provinces.

of other premises in Pope's Court. It is evident that no business was being carried on that day in the City; the day was a Monday; therefore the day was Bank Holiday Monday. This unusual date was, doubtless, expressly chosen so that neither Wilson nor Spaulding should have any pressing reason for staying in Saxe-Coburg Square. We must remember that it was important, from the conspirators' point of view, that *both* men should be free to attend at Pope's Court, not merely so as to avoid delay and error in getting hold of the right Jabez Wilson, but also so that Spaulding[1] should be at hand to influence his employer's decision by offering to attend to the business in his absence.

It is, no doubt, odd that Wilson should not have mentioned to Holmes that the interview took place on Bank Holiday; but in his flustered state of mind the fact had probably slipped his memory, nor was there any reason why he should attach special importance to it. It may, perhaps, be a small corroborative point that he waited until the morning following the interview before effecting the purchase of a penny bottle of ink, a quill pen and seven sheets of foolscap. True, he was in low spirits on the Monday evening, but, on the other hand, he had returned from Pope's Court in a state of joyful excitement, and Spaulding might well have suggested the immediate purchase of the stationery, had any shops been open at the time. I do not, however, insist upon this. The most interesting and suggestive point in the narrative is, I submit, the absence of a shop-window combined with the putting-up of the shutters. It will be noticed, by the way, that the shutters were 'put up for the day', although (until he saw the crowds) Wilson could have had no reason to suppose that the interview would occupy more than a couple of hours at most. Evidently he had determined to make a day of it in any case; and this adds further weight to the argument for Bank Holiday.

NOTE ON DR WATSON'S HANDWRITING

The only document we possess, purporting to be in the handwriting of Dr Watson, is the sketch-map which illustrates the

---

[1] Spaulding would, indeed, miss a few hours of valuable time from his tunnelling work under the empty Bank, but this would be considered of minor importance, compared with the necessity of carrying through the plot to get Wilson out of the way.

adventure of *The Priory School*.[1] It bears his name in block letters at the right-hand bottom corner, and presents at first sight an aspect of authenticity. The wording is clear, and the letters, on the whole, neatly formed, though five out of the ten small 'i's are undotted, the small 'r' is loopless and tends to degenerate into a single stroke, the capital 'E' resembles a 'C', and there are variations in the forms of the capitals 'R' and 'T'. In any case, whoever executed this wording would, of course, be taking particular pains to make it legible and suitable for reproduction as a line-block, and it probably is very unlike the same person's hand when writing ordinary MS. or notes.

But is the writing necessarily that of Dr Watson? In *The Naval Treaty* we find a sketch-plan in exactly the same handwriting, purporting to have been drawn by Percy Phelps. In *The Golden Pince-nez* the identical handwriting again makes its appearance, masquerading this time as that of Stanley Hopkins.

It is possible, of course, that Watson himself re-drew the two last-mentioned sketches for the blockmaker, though since he evidently had access to Holmes' collection of original documents (e.g. the letter reproduced in *The Reigate Squires*), there is no obvious reason why he should have done so. It may be urged that at the time of *The Naval Treaty* (1888) he was married and not living in Baker Street; but this does not apply to *The Golden Pince-nez*, which belongs to 1894, the year of Holmes' return.

The probability is that all three of the plans—hurriedly executed on scraps of paper—reached the blockmaker in a crumpled and dirty condition unsuitable for reproduction, and were re-drawn by him from the originals. Or, since the same artist illustrated the whole series of stories, from the *Adventures* to the *Return*, he may have done the re-drawing.

The letter in *The Reigate Squires* is in a different category. The exact reproduction of the original handwritings was essential, and, although we know that it was badly crumpled during Holmes' struggle with Alec Cunningham, it was, of course, carefully ironed out and preserved as an important piece of evidence in the case; the blockmaker had to do his best with it.

It is a very curious thing that the handwriting on the blotting-paper in *The Missing Three-Quarter* should also bear a suspicious

[1] *The Strand Magazine*, February 1904.

resemblance to that of this ubiquitous calligrapher. It is supposed, on this occasion, to be the autograph of Godfrey
Staunton, written on a telegraph form with 'a broad-pointed
quill pen', and blotted with 'thin' post-office blotting-paper.
For a document produced under these conditions, it is remark-
ably legible, and the ink has spread very little.

Finally, in the definitive ('Omnibus') edition of 1928, the
signature 'John H. Watson' has been omitted from the map of
the Priory School. This cannot be without significance. Watson
doubtless felt its presence to be misleading, and had it excised
from the block as a tacit admission that neither sketch nor
writing was from his own hand.

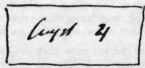

FIG. 1. *Dr. Watson's writing of August 4th (Augst. 4).* Note the formation of the "g"
(loopless), the ill-shaped "s" and the uncrossed "t"; also the preliminary flourish
to the left-hand stroke of the "4."

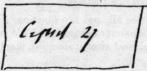

FIG. 2. *Dr. Watson's writing of April 27th.* Note the "pr" without loop and the
undotted "i."

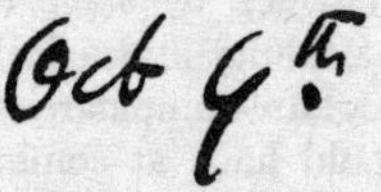

$$Oct \ 4^{th}$$

FIG. 3. *Ross's suggested method of writing "October 4th."*

➤✳ 7 ✳◄

ARTHUR MARSHALL

'RING FOR OUR BOOTS'

How often do we quote Doctor Watson, but how sadly few are the details about him that we can call to mind. We remember his indignant outbursts and his cry of 'Good Heavens, Holmes! This is intolerable,' on hearing that their rooms at 221B Baker Street have been set on fire by Professor Moriarty. We remember his tendency ('My head is in a whirl') to be somewhat easily baffled. We remember, of course, his firm grasp of the obvious:

> Sherlock Holmes had not come back yet. It was nearly ten o'clock before he entered, looking pale and worn. He walked up to the sideboard, and, tearing a piece from the loaf, he devoured it voraciously. . . .
> 'You are hungry,' I remarked.

But this cannot be all, and two questions immediately present themselves: Whatever became of Mrs Watson (prominent in *The Sign of Four*), and what, if anything, was Doctor Watson's practice?

Indefatigable as he was in reporting at length over fifty of the cases, Doctor Watson inexcusably excites us by the mention of twenty-two of which we have nothing but the bare names. A little more assiduity and a little less harping on his leg (wounded in the Afghan Campaign and apt to throb in wet weather), and we should have at command such matters as Mrs Farintosh and the Opal Tiara, Ricoletti of the Club Foot and his Abominable Wife, The Singular Affair of the Aluminium Crutch, and The Tragedy of the Atkinson Brothers at Trincomalee. He tantalizes us further with The Vatican Cameos, The Sudden Death of Cardinal Tosca, The Card Scandal at the Nonpareil Club, and The Affair of the Bogus Laundry (the mangles, one supposes, were disguised counterfeiting apparatus). Watson could hardly claim, as you shall see, that marital or professional obligations encroached seriously upon his time. Nor will the plea that some of the cases were 'complete failures' appeal to the amateurs among us. We know the correct methods, then let us apply them to the affair of 'Isadore Persano, the well-known journalist and duellist, who was found stark staring mad with a match-box in front of him which contained a remarkable worm, said to be unknown to science.'

But to Watson's marriage. Despite 'an experience of women which extends over many nations and three separate continents' it is to Lower Camberwell that Doctor Watson comes for his bride and to the house of a Mrs Cecil Forrester. Within is a 'needy governess' with blue eyes, Miss Mary Morstan, attired, for our first view, in 'sombre, greyish beige . . . and a small turban of the same dull hue'. The Doctor, badly smitten, has 'never looked upon a face which gave a clearer promise of a refined and sensitive nature'. The respectability of Lower Camberwell plays its part in the furthering of the romance:

> As we drove away, I stole a glance back, and I still seem to see that little group on the step—the two graceful, clinging figures, the half-opened door, the hall-light shining through stained glass, the barometer and the bright stair-rods. It was soothing to catch even that passing glimpse of a tranquil English home.

Miss Morstan is similarly enraptured with the Doctor, with his moustache and his square jaw and the Afghan tales which enliven his conversation. Her joy, poor girl, is brief. Her share of the Agra Treasure is dropped, bauble by bauble, into the Thames by Jonathan Small, and after a few months of married life in Paddington ('complete happiness' though it was) the Doctor, hot for Holmes, leaves her repeatedly. Occasionally, before departure, he 'dashes upstairs' to inform her, but once in Baker Street she is totally forgotten. Small wonder that latterly she is often 'away upon a visit' or 'on a visit to her aunt's'. We can but admire her demeanour: loving and dutiful to the end, she fades gradually from the picture, playing graciously into her selfish husband's hands ('Oh, Anstruther would do your work for you. You have been looking a little pale lately. I think the change would do you good. . . .') And so into oblivion in what manner we do not know, curtly dismissed in a passing reference to 'my recent sad bereavement'.

But, once in Baker Street, what chance would even an experienced charmer have had against the fascinator in the 'mouse-coloured dressing-gown'? The world is well lost indeed when Holmes springs to his feet crying, 'Ring for our boots and tell them to order a cab.' And off the hansom jingles to Stepney or Covent Garden or Bloomsbury or Holborn, or even to Saxe-Coburg Square. There are trips to Croydon, the Cornish Peninsula, Brixton Workhouse, and 'the pretty Surrey village of Esher'. There are thrilling peeps into private houses: The Myrtles, Beckenham; Laburnum Villa, Hammersmith; or Briarbrae, Woking. Every call was obediently answered: 'Come at once if convenient', telegraphs Holmes, 'if inconvenient come all the same', and off scuttles the Doctor, complete with jemmy and dark lantern and chisel, to Goldini's Restaurant, Gloucester Road. London, the outer suburbs and the southern counties are the most productive; there appears to have been little serious crime (*The Stockbroker's Clerk*) farther north than Birmingham. Back in Baker Street, with the Borgia jewel deftly prised from the last of the six Napoleon busts, there can be no thought of rest: 'Put the pearl in the safe, Watson,' orders Holmes, 'and get out the papers of the Conk-Singleton forgery case.'

A less-devoted slave might well have found some of Holmes' habits a little wearing to the nerves. The constant 'ping' of the hypodermic and the frequent snatches upon the violin (a Stradivarius, picked up in the Tottenham Court Road for fifty-five shillings) would perhaps have been bearable if they had been the only idiosyncrasies. They were not. There were the 'weird and often malodorous scientific experiments' and, more alarmingly, the 'occasional revolver practice within doors'. There were the 'devouring of sandwiches at irregular hours' and the tendency to awaken Watson before dawn on frosty winter mornings (insupportable, even if it meant a trip to Chislehurst). There were the biting of the nails, the times when he 'ran out and ran in', the refusal to make small-talk with the chatty Doctor, the clouds of the strongest shag tobacco. There was, horror of horrors, a recital at the St. James' Hall with Holmes 'gently waving his long thin fingers in time to the music'.

To offset these failings, Watson had, it must be allowed, much to intrigue him in Holmes' conversation. One's own reminiscences, even when about Afghanistan, are apt to pall and Holmes could hold forth on matters other than crime, passing lightly from severed thumbs to Warships of the Future, from clubbed skulls to the Bertillon System of Measurements, from suffocated peeresses to Miracle Plays. Watson had to learn about The Polyphonic Motets of Lassus and both Mediaeval and Chinese Pottery (including 'the marks of the Hung-wu and the beauties of the Yung-lo and the writings of Tang-ying'). To what extent the good Doctor's education had been previously neglected we cannot say. He can bring out a Latin quotation of fourteen words, but of his school days we know nothing except that he had been 'intimately associated with a lad named Percy [or 'Tadpole'] Phelps', nephew of Lord Holdhurst, and that it had been considered 'piquant' to 'chevy him about the playground and hit him over the shins with a wicket'. We can, perhaps, safely assume that Holmes, with his instructive chatter, was not wasting his time. Phelps turns up again at the time of *The Naval Treaty* when 'he was still weak after his long illness and his misfortunes made him querulous and nervous'. Doctor Watson advances upon the invalid and endeavours ('in vain', alas) to distract him with tales of (can you guess?) Afghanistan.

One would, I think, hardly have cared to be one of Doctor Watson's patients. He was so seldom there. However, there was at first some pretence of being concerned with medicine, and he purchased 'a connection in the Paddington district' from 'Old Mr Farquhar'. The tottering practice (Old Mr Farquhar suffered from 'an affliction of the nature of St. Vitus' Dance') had three advantages: it was better than the practice next door (Holmes observed that the step was worn three inches lower), there was a convenient substitute at hand, and it was near a station where 'railway cases were seldom trivial'. For three months he worked hard but the wretched man's heart was never in it ('My practice is never very absorbing.') and after that it was simply fits and starts, cases 'of great gravity' and 'pressing professional business' alternating with absences of days at a time. How listless the bed-side manner must have been. Sometimes even Holmes points out the path of duty: 'You want to go home, no doubt, Doctor?' 'Yes, it would be as well', but of course he is shortly back, armed, in Baker Street, and sipping from 'the spirit case and gasogene' until all hours. A Kensington practice follows (from which he is secretly bought out by Holmes) and after that there is no more pretence, though he does sometimes take down a volume from his 'small medical shelf' and is always ready, should Holmes require it, with a diagnosis. Nor does his hand lose its cunning: asked by Holmes why Professor Presbury should move so mysteriously and on all fours down dark passages, Watson is not for a moment at a loss: 'Lumbago', he replies. It is not one of Holmes' tetchy days: 'We can hardly accept lumbago' is the only admonishment.

So it is back to Baker Street, in glorious permanence, with the fog swirling outside and cold partridge and Montrachet for supper, and the test tubes and the hydrochloric acid and 'the newly framed picture of General Gordon' to feast the eyes on, and the visits to the Turkish bath where Holmes is 'less reticent and more human than anywhere else' and cases can be discussed 'over a smoke in the pleasant lassitude of the drying-room'. And there are the occasional visits to Holmes' brother, Mycroft, and the sight of the 'beshawled and bediamonded' ladies outside the Lyceum. And there is the agreeable flutter of Holmes being offered a knighthood in 1902, and the solid comfort of knowing that one is John H. Watson, MD (why did his wife call him James?), late Indian Army, who played Rugger for Blackheath and was once thrown into the crowd at the Old Deer Park by 'Big Bob Ferguson'. There are, to be sure, occasional clouds. When in teasing mood, Holmes can reply to an over-simple deduction by the Doctor with 'Excellent, Watson! You scintillate today.' But the mood was not always so. Even though he is feigning delirium (in *The Dying Detective*) Holmes comes out with some unpleasant truths: 'Facts are facts, Watson, and after all you are only a general practitioner with very limited experience and mediocre qualifications.' It does not need the Doctor to tell us that he is 'bitterly hurt'.

But he has his reward at last. He finds that he is more than the useful errand-boy, the bottle-washer, the willing horse. He is wounded in a shooting affray and Holmes, thinking the

wound more serious than it is, allows something to pierce the
bleak façade:

> My friend's wiry arms were round me and he was leading
> me to a chair.
> 'You're not hurt, Watson? For God's sake, say that you are
> not hurt.'
> It was worth a wound—it was worth many wounds—
> to know the depth of loyalty and love which lay behind that
> cold mask. The clear, hard eyes were dimmed for a moment,
> and the firm lips were shaking. For the one and only time I
> caught a glimpse of a great heart as well as of a great brain.
> All my years of humble but single-minded service culminated
> in that moment of revelation.

Exactly. And what chance had poor Miss Mary Morstan against
a moment such as that?

BERNARD DARWIN

SHERLOCKIANA: THE FAITH
OF A FUNDAMENTALIST

I am a Fundamentalist. A number of learned persons have
written books on Sherlock Holmes, proving from the dates that
the events recorded in the sacred text of Dr Watson did not
happen and could not have happened at the time and in the
order in which we have been led to believe; that Professor
Moriarty, for instance, could not have been plotting devilry at
Birlstone Manor in 1899 if he had tumbled over the Reichenbach Falls in 1891. Some of them even push profanity so far as
to allege that the Doctor, at a time when we sympathized with
him as mourning the first Mrs Watson (nee Morstan), must in
fact have married a second wife, possibly Miss Violet de Merville. I have read these authors, or some of them, with interest,
and even with a certain reluctant admiration for their diabolical
cleverness, to say nothing of their industry. It is the same sort
of admiration as that with which one watches a conjurer, conscious of one's own incapacity either to emulate him or to
understand how he does it. They have, thank heaven, written
no wrinkle on my innocent brow, nor affected my orthodoxy in
the slightest degree. I still believe that the various adventures
occurred exactly in the order in which they were told to us—
A Study in Scarlet first, *The Sign of Four* second, *A Scandal in
Bohemia* third, and so on down to *The Retired Colourman*. The
evidence of the dates troubles me no more than the incon-
testable evidence of the rocks troubles those who believe that
the world was created in a precise order in the course of six
days. If there is some little confusion or disagreement between
them it is not for me and others of the true faith to try to reconcile or explain them. I continue to read the stories over and
over again with an undisturbed mind. I do not wish to be un-

charitable and so to condemn the commentators as very wicked people; I regard them merely as misguided, and all their daring and brilliancy slip off me as easily as water off a duck's back.

At the same time, in so far as it is possible to study the stories without doubting any fundamental truths or too grossly emending a possibly faulty text, it seems to me licit to do so, and there are one or two points on which I have views, and even theories, however humble. I have not read all the commentators, and it may be that I am like poor Mr Casaubon, 'groping about in woods with a pocket compass while they have made good roads'. Nevertheless, I will venture on one or two remarks. I have always been interested in the question of Holmes' university career and have lately re-read once again Miss Dorothy Sayers' essay on the subject. It is an erudite, almost a monumental work, giving proof of the most scrupulous research; and yet it seems to me that she has founded her views too exclusively on the vital passages in *The Gloria Scott* and *The Musgrave Ritual* and not paid sufficient attention to the other stories dealing with university life.

With her conclusion that Holmes was at Cambridge I respectfully agree, and the more gladly because it is my own university. Even as the 'curious incident of the dog in the night-time' was of vast importance in the case of Silver Blaze, so the incident of the bull terrier is here decisive, as Miss Sayers, following Father Ronald Knox, points out. The argument runs briefly thus. Victor Trevor's bull terrier 'froze on to' Holmes' ankle one morning as he 'went down to Chapel'. The dog would not be allowed in college, therefore the incident happened outside, while Holmes was on his way from his lodgings. Holmes was up for only two years. If he had been at Oxford he would have spent his first two years in college. If he had been at Cambridge he would have begun in lodgings and only come into college in his third year. Q.E.D.

It is when Miss Sayers tentatively suggests that Holmes' college was Sidney that she is on much less sure ground. In fact, I do not believe any Cambridge man will agree with her. The question hinges on Reginald Musgrave, who was undoubtedly at the same college as Holmes. Musgrave was 'of an exceedingly aristocratic type' and 'a scion of one of the very oldest families in the Kingdom'. Holmes could never look at him without thinking of grey archways and mullioned windows. He was a considerable landowner and 'always a bit of a dandy'. With all possible respect for every one concerned, Sidney would not have been his college. Granted Miss Sayers' assumption that the college was a small one, then there is an obvious choice, Magdalene, 'that horsy home of revel' as it is called in *Horace at the University of Athens*. That is to be sure only a guess, but it is a much better guess than Sidney.

Now to turn back for a moment to the general question of which was Holmes' university, is there anything to be gleaned from *The Creeping Man*, *The Missing Three-Quarter*, and *The Three Students*? From the first, I think nothing, for the university is disguised as Camford, and the fact that Holmes remembered the inn there and that 'the port used to be above mediocrity' gets us no further, though the words 'used to be' point to recollections of undergraduate days. In *The Missing Three-Quarter* the university is definitely named as Cambridge, and that being so it is a little odd that when Holmes goes there, as he does, to prosecute his researches, he does not mention it as his *Alma Mater* and shows no emotion or interest in re-visiting it. It is true that he says to Watson, 'You are not familiar with Cambridgeshire scenery, are you?' and that might be held to imply his own familiarity with it; but as he had just returned from some hours of bicycling through the county it is not conclusive.

It is when we come to *The Three Students* that difficulties thicken. The university is not named and the college is St Luke's. The tutor's room, as Watson specifically states, looked on to 'the ancient lichen-tinted Court'. That points to Cambridge, and yet a little later Holmes remarks, 'We will take a walk in the Quadrangle,' which as definitely points to Oxford. Watson would not know the difference between the two langu-ages, but Holmes unquestionably would. Yet it might be that, although St Luke's was at Cambridge, Holmes used the word 'Quadrangle', which came natural to him as an Oxford man. It makes me a little uneasy, but not nearly so uneasy as the fact that Holmes talked about 'the three students'. Moreover, in *The Musgrave Ritual* he had referred to his 'old fellow-students' at the university. Now this is a really serious matter. Would any one who had been at either Oxford or Cambridge talk of students in that connection? To me that is not to be thought of. He might have called them men or undergraduates or anything but students. It is so incredible that at one time I almost came to think that Holmes' university career was a figment of his imagination.

Mr A. G. Macdonnell declared that Holmes had invented Moriarty, or rather had 'selected a perfectly ordinary ex-professor and fastened on to the unfortunate man the fearful reputation which has dogged him ever since'. My supposition is not nearly so blasphemous as that, but luckily there is for the faithful a reasonable way out. Watson himself was at London University and might well use the word 'students'. Furthermore, though he knew it was not the correct term to put in the mouth of Holmes, he might think it permissible to do so because the word would be more intelligible to his myriad readers who had not had Holmes' advantages. That will have to do, and I think it suffices. So Holmes was a Cambridge man, and all is well with the world.

Apropos of colleges and youthful pursuits, I have always wished to know more of Dr Watson's career as a football player, but there is so very little material. All we know (from *The Sussex Vampire*) is that he played for Blackheath when Big Bob Ferguson played three-quarter for Richmond, and once threw Watson over the ropes at the Old Deer Park. Where did Watson play? Not three-quarter or he would have mentioned it. Neither was he fast enough, for though he once declared that he had been 'reckoned fleet of foot', Holmes completely outpaced him in that wild chase after the Hound across Dartmoor. Full back perhaps, a post for which his 'admirable tenacity' might have fitted him, but I doubt it. He was a good, solid, hard-working forward who put his head down and pushed without too much thought. Apparently he had ceased to follow the game after his playing days were over; otherwise when the captain of the Cambridge fifteen asked despairingly what to do in the absence of his crack three-quarter, Godfrey Staunton, Watson would have had some suggestion to make. As it was he showed remarkable modesty in not referring to his feats on the Rectory Field; but what I want to know is what he was doing at Blackheath at all, when he ought to have been playing for Bart's or the United Hospitals. The hospital must have had first call on his services. This lack of loyalty is disturbing. However, we know that after his student days he was either a house surgeon or house physician at Bart's, and it was then presumably when no longer qualified to play for his hospital that Blackheath claimed him.

Now I have a word to say about a little social peculiarity of Holmes. We always think of him as a man of a highly democratic turn of mind, who almost too consciously spurned personages of high rank. He turned brusquely away when the King of Bohemia extended his hand to him; he appeared to be bored with the long list of a Duke's titles; he refused a knighthood. When Watson was much impressed by the crest on a letter, Holmes remarked, 'I assure you without affectation that the status of my client is a matter of less moment to me than the interest of his case.' And yet I have always had a notion that this was to some extent a pose. In his secret heart I believe that he had social aspirations, and that when in looking at Reginald Musgrave he thought of mullioned windows and feudal keeps, he longed for some more exalted lineage than the country squires whom he claimed as his ancestors. Probably this longing increased as his practice took him into higher spheres.

This is only a guess, but it is certainly curious that in his earlier days he was ignorant of some simple social usages. When Lord Robert St Simon came to consult him, he said genially, 'Good day, Lord St Simon. Pray take the basket chair,' and continued thus to refer to him. But somebody must have told him of this little solecism, and it was not Watson, who was himself guilty of it. Perhaps he privately looked up the point in a book of etiquette, which told him how to address letters to the nobility. At any rate, he found out and was later inclined to go too far in the opposite direction. In the case of Charles Augustus Milverton, that blackmailer in high life, Holmes laboriously alluded to his client as '*The* Lady Eva Brackwell'. It was the same in the case of the unfortunate Lady Frances Carfax, who was so nearly buried alive. 'Ah, what has happened to the Lady Frances?' he exclaimed passionately, and kept it up throughout. He was not to be caught napping again and called the Duke of Holdernesse 'Your Grace' with the utmost punctilio and almost wearisome iteration. That is the trouble about converts; they will overdo it.

But the subject is perhaps too painful and embarrassing. Let me turn to another redounding almost wholly to Holmes' glory. Has full credit ever been given him for his constant and successful antagonism to the Germans? At the beginning of the last war Dr Goebbels and his associates prayed English literature in aid for a violent attack on Mr Churchill. They made a not notably apt comparison between him and Quilp. They overlooked the fact that their real enemy in literature was beyond question Sherlock Holmes. They cannot possibly have forgotten *His Last Bow*. Only a sense of humiliation must here have kept them silent, for, as is well known, Holmes, in the disguise of an American with a chin beard, utterly bamboozled their master spy, Von Bork, palmed off on him a mass of false information as to the Fleet, trussed him up with the help of the faithful Watson and added insult to injury first by drinking his best Tokay and then cashing a cheque for £500 handed to Holmes for his supposed treachery.

That was the most conspicuous example, but it is really remarkable on how many other occasions he opposed some German villain or villainess, as a rule to their disadvantage. In his first encounter he was not wholly successful: Irene Adler, though born in New Jersey, presumably had German blood in her veins, and she got rather the best of him, even if his client, the King of Bohemia, was entirely satisfied. Next came Colonel Lysander Stark, who cut off Mr Hatherley's thumb. That was obviously not his real name, for he spoke 'with something of a German accent'. Incidentally, the alias must have appealed to Holmes, for some time later, in *The Three Garridebs*, he himself invented an imaginary person with a very similar name, Dr Lysander Starr. Holmes was not deceived by the Colonel's wiles and easily discovered the hiding place where he had been counterfeiting coin; but it must be admitted that after that he failed. How several people in a heavily loaded cart, one of them with a German accent, entirely vanished in the middle of Berkshire is a discreditable mystery.

Holmes was far more successful in the realm of high politics. In the matter of *The Second Stain* there can be no question as to the foreign potentate who wrote the indiscreet letter, the publication of which was calculated to plunge the country into war. Of course it was the Kaiser. Holmes wrote down a name on a piece of paper and the Prime Minister replied, 'Exactly.' Holmes got the letter back and no harm was done.

He was equally triumphant in the case of the plans of the Bruce-Partington submarine. Can anybody doubt that it was the German navy to whom they were to be sold? The very name of the agent involved, Oberstein, is almost conclusive. Holmes made a complete fool of Mr Oberstein, who came obediently, bringing in his sheaves with him, to the smoking-room of the Charing Cross Hotel, where doubtless Lestrade, that trusty bulldog, awaited him.

Then at the bidding of that *Illustrious Client*, at whose identity we can only make a reverent guess, Holmes outwitted the unspeakable Baron Gruner, robbed him of his infamous brown book and saved Miss de Merville. He was not equally successful in the case of another book, the novel which Douglas Maberley had written about Isadora Klein, but at least he blackmailed her to the tune of £5,000 for his client's benefit (*The Three Gables*). True, Isadora was Spanish, 'the real blood of the masterful Conquistadors', as Holmes observed in a sudden gush of romantic language, but she had married an aged German Sugar King, and so may fairly be added to Holmes' German bag. The Russians are now trying to ban him on the ground of his capitalistic tendencies, but he never did them any harm. The rascal who pretended to be a Russian nobleman in *The Resident Patient* was neither the one nor the other. It is the poor, ponderous Germans who were consistently outwitted by him. True, I had almost forgotten one item on the other side of the account. Holmes alleged that he had saved from murder at the hands of the Nihilist, Klopman, Count Von and Zu Grafenstein, a relative of Von Bork's. We take his word for it since that story is one with those of the Paradol Chamber and the Giant Rat of Sumatra. They were used to tantalize his Boswell but were never told.

I have set down a few of the thoughts, 'elementary, my dear Watson,' as I am too well aware, that have occurred to me in some fifty-five years of persistent reading. Even a Fundamentalist may have his preferences among the sacred writings, and as to the short stories at any rate I have no doubt that the spring time was best. In his preface to the collected edition Sir Arthur Conan Doyle expressed the hope that the reader,

The former long bar
at the Criterion,
Piccadilly Circus, where
Watson met the friend
who was to introduce
him to Holmes.

'Then he stood
before the fire'

Inside 221B Baker Street.
Sidney Paget's first drawing
of the famous sitting-room
for *A Scandal in Bohemia*.

The Strand, looking west. Holmes and Watson took a memorable three-hour stroll along the Strand and Fleet Street in *The Resident Patient*.

being able to take the stories in any order, would 'not find that the end shows any conspicuous falling off from the modest merits of the beginning'. It would be pleasant but it is impossible to agree. In one respect there is something to be said for this view. The clash of temperaments between Watson and Holmes becomes more noticeable in the later stories and Watson's character shows a marked development. In early days he muttered 'Brag and bounce' to himself when he was annoyed by Holmes' vanity, but he knew better than to speak his thoughts aloud. Later he developed, as Holmes himself noted, 'a certain unexpected vein of pawky humour' at the Master's expense. This in its turn produced such pleasing retaliations as (on two occasions), 'You are scintillating this morning.' 'Perhaps there are points which have escaped your Machiavellian intellect.' 'Watson, I have always done you an injustice. There are others'—and so on. These little bouts of thrust and parry are more frequent as the stories go on, and add a zest to life, though it must be owned that Holmes' weapon was more often the bludgeon than the rapier. Yet they do not wholly make up for something of lost freshness. That freshness may have been not in the early stories but in the reader himself. It may belong to a time when his love was purer and less critical, when perhaps he had not even begun to smile, however tenderly, at the two great creatures. It is so hard to recall the sensation of that first breath-taking plunge into delights, grown long since familiar. The Fundamentalist always goes back to the Book of Genesis, and I always return to the stories enshrined in the earliest volumes of *The Strand*. They are the impregnable rock on which my faith is founded.

9

E. V. KNOX

THE PASSING OF SHERLOCK HOLMES

The death is announced at North Friston, near Eastbourne, of
Mr Sherlock Holmes, the eminent Criminologist and Investigator, President of the South Sussex Apiarist Society, and
Corresponding Secretary to the National Beekeepers' Union.
He was in his ninety-third year; and there is little doubt that
but for his characteristic disregard of the occupational risks of
this last hobby he would have lived to become a centenarian.

'The creatures know my methods,' he would often observe
to visitors as he walked without veil or gloves between the
orderly rows of his hives. Yet he over-estimated their obedience,
and it was an irritant poison caused by one of these dangerous
insects, possibly an Italian Queen, that undermined his iron
constitution in the end, and was the immediate occasion of his
demise.

His white hair and only slightly stooping figure had long
been objects of veneration both to the passing motorist and to
all residents of the countryside between Birling Gap and Newhaven.

He was particularly interested in the formation and history of
dew ponds, and might often have been seen returning to his
little farmhouse with a bundle of fossils taken from the chalk,
or a nosegay of downland flowers.

His later years were but little disturbed by occurrences
either terrible or bizarre, but we must except from this statement the sudden appearance (narrated by himself) of *Cyanea
Capillata*, the giant jellyfish, which, at the foot of the Seven
Sisters, stung to death Mr Fitzroy Macpherson and came very
near to baffling the old Investigator's deductive powers. Otherwise his closing years were passed in quietude. Every evening

82

he was accustomed to listen to the Third or the Home Programme of the BBC, especially the musical portions. For Light Programmes, and especially for the feature entitled 'Dick Barton', he was wont to express a profound contempt.

Sherlock Spencer Tracy Holmes was born in 1855, the second son of Sir Stateleigh Holmes of Carshalton in Surrey. The family was descended from a long line of country squires, and Sir Stateleigh's mother was the sister of Vernet, the French artist. Sherlock himself was educated at St Peter's School and Pembridge College, Camford, where the rooms he occupied (now held by the Director of Theological Studies in that college) are often pointed out with pride and gratification by the present Master.

He took little part in the academic or sporting life of his contemporaries and made few friends; but those whom he did know never forgot him and lived to be thankful for the fact. Two of the most eminent were the late Colonel Reginald Musgrave, MFH, of Hurlston, and Admiral Victor Trevor, KCB, both of whom he had assisted at critical junctures in their youth, and it is safe to say that but for these early acquaintanceships neither the whereabouts of the lost crown of Charles I nor the log-book of the *Gloria Scott* would ever have been made known to the public. It was, indeed, Admiral Trevor's father who actually suggested to Holmes in his early days the vocation which he afterwards so brilliantly followed, using the following remarkable prophetic words: 'I don't know how you managed this, Mr Holmes, but it seems to me that all the detectives of fact and of fancy would be children in your hands. That's your line of life, sir; and you may take the word of a man who has seen something of the world.'

He spoke no more than the truth. Dying a few months later, with little more time than to say that the papers were in the back drawer of the Japanese cabinet, Mr Trevor could not foresee that his son's friend was destined to become almost a legendary figure, the hero and idol of two generations of mankind, and the scourge of evil-doers throughout what was once called the civilized globe.

No detective can have travelled more widely than the late Mr Holmes, nor on errands so mysterious, not to say sinister, and verging on the grotesque. Summoned to Odessa to un-

ravel the Trepoff murder, he was equally successful in solving
the tragedy of the Atkinson brothers at Trincomalee. Rome
knew him at the inquiry into the sudden death of Count
Tosca. Lyons, when he had penetrated the colossal scandals of
Baron Maupertuis in connection with the Netherland Sumatra
Company. In the interval between his supposed death in
Switzerland and his reappearance in London he made journeys
through Persia, looked in at Mecca, rendered assistance to the
Khalifa of Khartoum, visited Lhasa, and spent some time with
the Grand Lama of Tibet. It is a pity that the details of these
expeditions are for the most part wrapped in a veil of impene-
trable secrecy, which, unless the great tin box bequeathed to
the British Museum is opened by Mr Attlee or some future
Prime Minister, may never be lifted.

But in spite of these foreign pilgrimages, Holmes was able
to undertake in this country a series of investigations which
made him for more than twenty years, and later at intervals,
the terror of the metropolitan underworld, the knight-errant
of suburban London, and the constant corrector of the stupidi-
ties of Scotland Yard.

This department, especially during the middle 'nineties,
appears to have had only two consistent policies, of which the
first was complacent error and the second unutterable be-
wilderment. Holmes revolutionized its procedure, and we may
note as evidence of this that the old daguerreotypes of Athelney
Jones, Gregson, and Lestrade, which once adorned its portrait
gallery, have long ago had their faces turned to the wall. It is
a pity that the projected work by Assistant Commissioner
Stanley Hopkins, OBE, entitled 'My Master's Voice' remained
uncompleted at the time of the Nether Wallop Mystery, when
that able officer met his end after a dastardly assault from the
blow-pipe of a Nicaraguan dwarf.

If ever a man was called for to meet the hour, Sherlock
Holmes, in the heyday of his triumphs, was that man. For
England, during the last decade of the nineteenth century, was
in danger of submersion beneath an almost unprecedented wave
of crime. Criminals of Herculean strength and stature, gifted
with a well-nigh super-human cunning, had spread a network
of villainy throughout the land.

Blackmail and forgery were rife. The robbery of the most

famous piece of jewellery in the world was an almost hourly occurrence. Agents of mysterious secret societies, thirsting for revenge, haunted the docks and the purlieus of Soho. Wills and the plans of submarines were constantly disappearing, and no treaty with a foreign Power was safe for more than a moment in its desk.

To all these manifestations of the villainous and the macabre, Holmes opposed a technique, entirely novel and entirely his own. It may be subdivided and tabulated as follows:

1. Chemical Analysis; 2. Analytical Deduction; 3. Tobacco; 4. Bouts of Contemplation; 5. Feverish Energy; 6. The Minute Examination of Scratches; 7. Omniscience; 8. Cocaine.

And to these should possibly be added the cross-indexing of important cases, the music of the violin, the employment of a hoard of street Arabs as agents, and the constant use of the agony columns of the daily Press. The result was a purer air in the streets of London, a sense of relief in the suburbs from Kensington to Whitechapel, from Hampstead to Norwood, and the rescue of many an ill-used girl from death or worse than death in the Home Counties and the more distant provinces.

Repeatedly also the government of the day was saved from ruin. We need only mention in this connection the temporary loss of the Bruce Partington Submarine plans in 1895, and the fear that they might have been sold to a foreign Power. 'You may take it from me,' said Mr Holmes' brother in speaking of them, 'that naval warfare becomes impossible when in the radius of a Bruce Partington's operation.' Happily for the future of this country, Mr Holmes succeeded in recovering the plans.

By the close of the century, the agency which he established had become world-famous. Many were the nights when the feet of a flustered client would patter along the flagstones of Baker Street, or the spirited horse of some hastily driven four-wheeler would be reined to its haunches at his door.

The sound of his violin would float out into the foggy atmosphere, punctuated by the pistol shots with which he pockmarked the pattern VR from his sofa on the opposite wall of his sitting-room.

A bundle of letters from the sister of his landlady (recently discovered on a bomb-site) is ample evidence of the admiration not unmingled with awe which he inspired in the whole of her family.

But it is impossible to deal adequately with the great detective's achievements unless we acknowledge the peculiar debt that he owed during the greater part of his active career to his old friend and colleague, the late Lord Watson of Staines. Lord Watson, it will be remembered, died suddenly last year, after a particularly violent attack in the House of Lords upon certain provisions of the National Health Bill. Eminent alike as a physician and an orator, he is none the less even more likely to incur the gratitude of posterity as the constant companion and intermittent (though mystified) biographer of Mr Sherlock Holmes.

> '*How do you know that?*'
> '*I followed you.*'
> '*I saw no one.*'
> '*That is what you may expect to see when I follow you.*'

Yet indeed it was Lord Watson himself, wondering, shadowy, yet observant, who followed Holmes. Without him, Holmes would have remained a mysterious, almost a visionary character: known to the police forces of the world, familiar to the courts and the aristocracies of Europe, the condescending patron of Prime Ministers, and of the humbler clients whom he chose to assist, yet occult from the observation of the public at large. For publicity was a thing he disdained, and only in the case of Lord Watson, especially in the privacy of the rooms which they shared, did he throw off the mantle of obscurity that screened his personal habits from the eyes of men.

Never, we think, has so great a privilege been so enthusiastically enjoyed. Lord Watson was *par excellence* a hero-worshipper. He had nothing to learn of Plato or Boswell in this respect. To be baffled was his glory, to be astounded his perennial delight. Sitting with his medical dictionary just out of the line of pistol fire, he revelled in the deductive processes by which the great detective inferred the whole of a visiting client's character from a button, a whisker, a watch, or a boot. There are many who say that Lord Watson was an inaccurate historian. There are cavillers (and Holmes himself was one of them) who have suggested that he embellished fact with fiction, and dipped his brush in melodrama instead of depicting the portrait of a living man. It is impossible to pursue all these charges in detail. Yet one or two comments are not out of place.

Curiously enough, his biographer's presentation does not always redound to the advantage of Holmes. Lord Watson was bemused by metaphors. His mind was influenced beyond all reason by images of the chase. Time after time, for instance, he seems to have been obsessed with the idea that Mr Holmes was a kind of dog.

'As I watched him I was irresistibly reminded of a pure-blooded well-trained foxhound as it dashes backwards and forwards through the covert, whining in its eagerness until it comes across the lost scent. . . .'

'His nostrils seemed to dilate with a purely animal lust for the chase, and his mind was so absolutely concentrated upon the matter before him that a question or remark fell unheeded upon his ears, or at the most only provoked a quick impatient snarl in reply. . . .'

'He was out on the lawn, in through the window, round the room, and up into the bedroom, for all the world like a dashing foxhound drawing a cover. . . .'

'Like an old hound who hears the View Holloa. . . .'

Hard indeed it is to reconcile these phrases with the picture of the tall, dignified, sombrely-attired figure whom we know so well from his portraits in *The Strand Magazine*, dressed in frock coat or ulster; the finely chiselled features, the pale intellectual forehead surmounted by the silk or Derby hat. Even the deerstalker of his more rustic peregrinations does not warrant the perpetual comparison of Mr Holmes to a denizen of the hunting kennel: and we can only feel that idolatry has here overstepped its bounds, and trespassed on the realm of caricature.

On the other hand, Holmes (as stated in a previous paragraph) was omniscient. Lord Watson must have known this. Yet he denies it. He makes Holmes attribute this particular gift (or 'specialism' as he called it) to Sir Mycroft, the detective's elder brother, but Sherlock (as a hundred instances will testify) had it, too. Let a single example suffice.

From what motive one cannot guess, whether from envy or

for the sake of whimsical exaggeration, Lord Watson in one memoir states that Sherlock's knowledge of literature was *nil*. In another he makes Holmes quote Goethe twice, discuss miracle plays, comment on Richter, Hafiz and Horace, and remark of Athelney Jones: 'He has occasional glimmerings of reason. "*Il n'y a pas des sots si incommodes que ceux qui ont de l'esprit!*"'

It has even been conjectured, though wrongly, from this evidence of wide culture that Mr Holmes was attracted by the decadent aesthetic movement of the 'nineties. But a careful search through the pages of the *Yellow Book* fails to reveal any poem or prose contribution from his pen, and the whole tenor of his life seems to remove him entirely from the world in which Dowson, Symons and Aubrey Beardsley and the other ghosts of the old Café Royal lived and moved. He is never mentioned by Sir William Rothenstein or Sir Max Beerbohm in any of their reminiscences of the period. As a literary figure he remains enigmatic and aloof. Yet from Lord Watson's narrative, however melodramatic, however inaccurate, there does emerge the definite picture of a man; and (if we are prepared to make allowances for the occasional eccentricities of the writer) a man who must be very like the real Holmes.

To continue the actual narrative of his known career, Sherlock Holmes was offered a knighthood in 1902 but refused it. He took up government work in the period immediately preceding the First World War, and was instrumental in foiling the notorious Von Bork, one of the most devoted agents of the Kaiser. For this he was again offered a knighthood which he again refused.

He had a profound knowledge of chemistry, and a grip of iron, was an expert boxer and swordsman, and a voluminous writer. His most popular and widely-read works are those on *The Polyphonic Motets of Lassus*, his two short *Monographs on Ears*, originally published in the *Anthropological Journal*, his brochures on *The Tracing of Footsteps, with some Remarks upon the Uses of Plaster as a Preserver of Impresses*, his *Influence of a Trade on the Form of a Hand*, his *Essay on the Distinction of the Ashes of Various Tobaccos*, and his *Handbook of Bee Culture, with some Observations upon the Segregation of the Queen*.

It is one of fate's ironies that a failure to observe some of his own precepts, laid down in the last book, may have brought about the close of a life ever devoted to his country's good. His form and lineaments, together with those of Lord Watson, have long been familiar in waxen effigy at Madame Tussaud's Exhibition, not far from his old lodgings. A sturdy moralist, if not a devout churchman, he was also an ardent Democrat, a believer in the close union of the English-speaking races, a hater of the colour bar, and a despiser of the trappings of pomp and power. He may well have been said, in the words of Kipling, to have walked with kings nor lost the common touch. He was unmarried.

⇒❖ 10 ❖⇐

J. C. MASTERMAN

THE CASE OF THE GIFTED AMATEUR

Amongst all the talented officers of Scotland Yard Chief Detective Inspector Lestrade was both the most astute and the most successful—so at least he often gave me to understand.

Long after he had retired I used to visit him in the nursing home in Surrey in which he passed the last years of his life, and with the minimum of encouragement he would relate again the triumphs of himself, of Gregson, of Athelney Jones, of 'young' Stanley Hopkins and the rest of those heroes who had flourished in what he considered the palmy days of the Yard.

Yet, curiously enough, he seldom mentioned the name of Sherlock Holmes, with whom his name had been linked in my own early memories. This I found difficult to understand, and I even, at one time, harboured the unworthy suspicion that he was in some way jealous of the reputation of Holmes, Baker Street detective.

When I contrived to mention Holmes' name he would make a faintly deprecatory comment and pass on to another part of the saga of his own career. Rarely, very rarely, he was more communicative about a man—or men, for a certain Dr Watson had worked with Holmes in those bygone days—about whose doings I had an insatiable curiosity. Once only he related a story of the two to me.

'Mr Sherlock Holmes was a clever man in his way, but not nearly so clever as he thought himself, and as for that Watson—! My old chief at the Yard, I remember, used to call Mr Sherlock Holmes "the Gifted Amateur", though why I couldn't quite make out.

'You see, properly speaking, he wasn't an amateur at all, and as for being gifted—well—there were some of us at the Yard

90

that could have given him half a stone and a beating any day.'

Lestrade gave a wheezy chuckle of satisfaction.

'But he had some bright ideas, hadn't he? I suppose he was helpful to you now and then?'

'If you ask me,' retorted Lestrade, 'the boot was on the other leg. I can remember one case when I helped Holmes—and Watson, too, for that matter—out of a pretty tight jam—not that they were as grateful to me as they might have been.

'I'll tell you about it.'

It was in the year 1889, so far as I can remember, and it's in my mind that Mr Sherlock Holmes had been having rather a lean time—why, even that Watson could hardly find any cases to write about at that time (you know the Doctor used to write up his friend's cases for what they call publicity purposes nowadays).

When, therefore, the case of the Dark Diamond was handed over to me and I noticed that Dr Watson was connected with it in his professional capacity, it seemed to me that it was the only kind thing to do to let Holmes have a finger in the pie. I was a bit sorry for him, as you might say, besides I wasn't too sure that I could solve the mystery just as quickly and easily as I wanted to.

So I walked round to Baker Street somewhere about tea-time and found them both smoking in their room.

'Ah, Lestrade,' said Holmes in his high and mighty manner, 'you are often the harbinger of good tidings—what have you for me now?'

'I suppose Dr Watson has told you about this case of Rheinhart Wimpfheimer's diamond?' I asked. Holmes smiled.

'Watson's account is a trifle confused. I should be glad if you would run over the case so that I may have the salient facts before me; possibly I may be able to help you.'

The reports which I made in those days didn't miss much, so I read out the notes which I had already made.

Mr Rheinhart Wimpfheimer is well known as a man who has amassed a prodigious fortune in trade with the Orient; he is even better known as the greatest of all collectors of famous and curious jewels.

In this field only one other person can compare with him, and that is his younger brother, Mr Solomon Wimpfheimer, a wealthy bachelor residing in Albany. Between the two brothers a keen but friendly rivalry has always existed, but the elder's collection is believed to be incomparably the finer.

Mr Rheinhart Wimpfheimer is himself a widower, living in some luxury at his residence, 123 Great Cumberland Place. Apart from the servants his household consists of himself, his unmarried daughter, aged about twenty-five, and his private secretary, who assists him both in his business dealings and in his collecting.

Many of his possessions have already been given or loaned to museums, but some of the more precious are always kept in the house.

Among them all the famous Dark Diamond of Dungbura holds pride of place. So much is he attached to this wonderful stone that he carries it with him daily in a small chamois leather bag suspended from his neck. At night it is placed resting on the chamois leather bag on the table by his bedside.

'A moment, Lestrade,' Holmes interrupted me. 'Watson, pray pass me the third of those bulky volumes by your side.

'Ah—yes—I thought that there would be a note. The Dark Diamond of Dungbura, one of the most famous stones in the world owing to its size, its peculiar colour, and its history. How or when it appeared in Dungbura, which is on the confines of Tibet, and how it passed from there to Europe are unknown, but it has since found a place in several of the greatest collections.

'Whereas most precious stones have a sinister reputation this one is reputed invariably to bring happiness and good fortune to its possessor.

'But I interrupt your orderly narrative, Lestrade. Proceed, if you will.'

Early on Wednesday morning Mr Rheinhart Wimpfheimer was suddenly taken ill. His usual medical attendant was on holiday and our friend Dr Watson here was acting as his locum tenens. Dr Watson was urgently summoned to the house at about nine and diagnosed the case as one of brain fever—correct me if I am wrong, Doctor.

'That is quite correct; I prescribed the usual remedies and promised to call again in the evening.'

Dr Watson called again in the evening and on his arrival found Mr Wimpfheimer still unconscious. During the course of the visit, however, the patient had a short period of mental clarity and—I regret to say—vehemently expressed his desire to have the assistance of some physician more highly qualified than Dr Watson.

'Ah, well,' said Holmes, 'after all he is a cultured man of unlimited wealth, and the services of a general practitioner of limited experience and mediocre ability. . . .'

'Holmes, this is unworthy of you,' protested Watson. 'You yourself have failed to obtain immediate success on some occasions.'

'The dates?' replied Holmes acidly.

I hurried on with my report lest a quarrel should develop between the two friends. The patient relapsed into delirium and Dr Watson gave instructions to the nurse and wrote down the names and addresses of some of his eminent fellow practitioners. He then left the house.

'The time, Watson?' inquired Holmes.

'It was 7 p.m.,' replied Watson, a little sulkily. 'Mr Wimpfheimer is a collector of furniture and *objets d'art* of all kinds. I passed at least four grandfather clocks on the staircase and as all of them struck the time was somehow impressed on my memory.'

'Excellent, Watson. I am gratified that you are developing the power of observation. What happened next?'

A call was sent to Scotland Yard at ten o'clock this morning and I myself hurried round to 123 Great Cumberland Place, where I found the house in a state of great commotion. When Sir Euston Pancras, the brain-fever specialist, called that morning to examine the patient, it was observed by the valet that the Dark Diamond of Dungbura, which had lain on the table by the bedside the night before, had vanished.

'It was there at the time of your visit, Watson?' inquired Holmes.

'It was—I observed it lying on the chamois leather bag on the table.'

Between that time and the specialist's visit five persons entered the sickroom—the nurse who was on duty during the night, the nurse who relieved her this morning, the patient's confidential valet, his private secretary and his daughter.

'What steps have you taken?' inquired Holmes. 'Have you examined all these persons?'

No stone has been left unturned but the mystery seems insoluble. Of the five persons concerned none left the house except Miss Wimpfheimer, who drove in a hansom to visit her uncle in Albany and tell him of his brother's progress.

She left the house at about 9 p.m. and returned some three-quarters of an hour later.

These persons are, moreover, all above suspicion. The valet and the secretary have been with Mr Wimpfheimer for more than 10 years, the first nurse retired to sleep almost immediately after she left the sickroom, and the second nurse did not leave the sickroom after she came on duty.

The whole house has been searched from attic to cellar and the diamond is not in it.

I am forced to the conclusion that some burglar must have entered the room and abstracted the stone—but here again there are difficulties. There are double windows in all the rooms and an elaborate system of burglar alarms; moreover Mr Wimpfheimer has a dachshund to which he is devotedly attached; this animal never leaves him and sleeps in his bedroom. It is inconceivable that it should not have barked if a burglar had entered the room in the night-time.

Still, a burglar *must* have entered the room. The question is, how and when did he enter, and how did he escape.

You know my methods, Mr Holmes; apply them (I often gave Mr Sherlock Holmes pieces of advice of that kind, and I think they were useful to him). Perhaps you may have some suggestion to make as to how the crime was accomplished.

Mr Sherlock Holmes honoured me with one of his supercilious smiles.

'The case, my good Lestrade, though essentially a simple one, presents some features which are not without interest. I shall be glad to look into it for you.'

'And when will you be prepared to restore the diamond?' I asked with just the proper touch of sarcasm.

'Perhaps if you will honour Dr Watson and myself with your company at breakfast tomorrow—let us say at 9.30—I may have some information for you.'

I can see that room in Baker Street as clearly as though it was yesterday. When I returned the next morning Holmes, in his dressing gown, was sitting in his chair at one side in a cloud of smoke and Dr Watson was opposite him looking ill and worried.

Perhaps, I thought, that Jezail bullet, of which he was always talking, was giving him a twinge of pain. His stethoscope, an old-fashioned instrument, was lying beside him, as though he was just about to start on a round of visits. Holmes waved me to a seat.

'Let me briefly elucidate the case,' he began. 'Last night I called at Great Cumberland Place. Disguised as a veterinary surgeon, I explained that Mr Wimpfheimer had given me an appointment some days before to examine the dachshund, and I was immediately admitted to the sickroom.

'The windows give no appearance of having been opened for some weeks at least; the physical formation of the dachshund enabled me, furthermore, to make an examination of the carpet.'

'What was peculiarly noticeable about the carpet?' I asked.

'Nothing was noticeable about the carpet—that was peculiar. Your theory that a burglar must have entered the room is wholly untenable.'

He paused and placed the tips of his long fingers together.

'We have therefore certain incontrovertible facts. The diamond lay on the table when Watson paid his visit at 7 p.m.; it had disappeared when Sir Euston called at 10 in the morning; no burglar can have entered the room during that period; five persons, and five persons alone, entered the room during the night; all of them people of unimpeachable character; no one of them had any motive, so far as is known, for the theft.

'It is an old maxim of mine, however, that when the impossible has been excluded, whatever remains, however improbable, must be the truth. Therefore one of those five persons stole the diamond.'

'Amazing, Holmes,' exclaimed Watson. Holmes' pale face flushed a little at this compliment, but he continued his exposition.

'If we confine ourselves to the established facts we can carry the analysis further.

'The diamond has been stolen from the bedroom, and stolen by one of the five persons who entered the bedroom. It is not in the house and therefore it has been removed from the house. I is a fair deduction that the thief who took it from the bedroom also removed it from the house.

'Moreover, other considerations lead me to the same conclusion. No ordinary thief would choose the night when a trained and wakeful nurse sat at Mr Wimpfheimer's bedside to make a burglarious entry, and indeed no professional thief would even contemplate stealing the Dungbura diamond, for its peculiarities would make it impossible for the thief to dispose of it.

'I therefore come to the conclusion that this was no ordinary thief. One solution and one only remains, Lestrade, the stone was abstracted not for vulgar gain but in order that it might be transferred to some other collection!

'There are no lengths to which collectors will not go—the pride of possession overcomes all scruples—and remember that the Dungbura diamond brings happiness and good fortune to its possessor.'

He paused dramatically.

'Mr Solomon Wimpfheimer is a collector. Miss Wimpfheimer visited him in the evening to tell him of his brother's illness. We do not know what impelled this unhappy woman to transfer the diamond from her father to her uncle, but we do know that it was her hand which removed it from Great Cumberland Place.

'The case is completed. Breakfast can wait. Put on your hat, Watson, and we will stroll with Lestrade to Albany. There, unless I am much mistaken, we shall find the diamond.'

'But, but—' interrupted Watson. Holmes frowned at his friend. 'I have demonstrated that the diamond can have left Great Cumberland Place in no other way,' he remarked severely.

'But—my stethoscope—' stammered Watson. We both turned towards him as the doctor, clutching his side, appeared to faint and fell back in his chair.

For the first time in my experience Holmes seemed to be overcome by a human emotion. He rushed to his friend, tore open his shirt and applied the stethoscope to his chest.

'Alas, poor fellow,' he cried, 'he is dead. I can hear nothing.'

'That,' muttered Watson, 'is what you must expect to hear when you use *my* stethoscope.'

For my part I seized a bottle of seltzogene from the table and dashed it over the doctor's face. He gradually recovered, though he still clutched his side as though in great pain. It was

Piccadilly on a fine sunny morning. Some of Holmes' cases brought him to the West End. His brother, Mycroft, had rooms in Pall Mall.

Fleet Street in the Holmes period had at least seven evening newspapers
compared with two today. In *The Blue Carbuncle* Holmes told
Peterson, the commissionaire, to put an advertisement in 'the
*Globe, Star, Pall Mall, St James's Gazette, Evening News, Standard,
Echo*, and any others that occur to you'.

then that I had one of those flashes of intuition which helped me so much in my career.

'Mr Holmes,' I said, 'I believe that Dr Watson has something which he wishes to say to us.' The doctor nodded assent.

'Holmes,' he said. 'I cannot keep silence any longer. I have been in the Army and it is impossible for me to allow a breath of suspicion to rest on a pure and lovely woman. At all costs I must clear her reputation.

'When Mr Wimpfheimer dismissed me in such cavalier fashion I felt a not unnatural resentment. At that moment, as he relapsed again into delirium, my eye caught the glint of the diamond lying on its chamois leather bag on the table. The nurse left us to bring in some cooling drink which I had prescribed.

'In a flash my mind was made up—indeed my brain seemed to function with abnormal speed and certainty. A complete plan presented itself to me. I would seize the diamond and convey it to Baker Street; you would find it in our room.

'I had no doubt that your keen analytical brain would connect the presence of the diamond in Baker Street with my visit to Great Cumberland Place, but I felt assured that the staunchiness of your friendship would shield me from any undesirable consequences.

'I felt certain that you would find means, when a baffled Scotland Yard consulted you, to restore the stone to its owner and to prove that it could in fact never have left Great Cumberland Place; you would then, I knew, generously allow Lestrade to take all the credit of the recovery.

'With me, to think is to act. To seize the diamond was the matter of a moment; I rolled it into its bag and thrust them both into the mouth of my stethoscope.

'Thus burdened, I hurried from the house and hailed the first passing hansom. Inside I felt for the first time a spasm of nervousness, and I doubted the security of the hiding place which I had chosen.

'I therefore removed the diamond from the bag, pushed the bag back into the stethoscope and placed the diamond in my mouth—a trick of concealment which I learned on the Afghan frontier.

'Then another doubt assailed me. It was essential for the

success of my plan that you should not fail to find the diamond. Should I place it in the tobacco in your Persian slipper (but you might not smoke enough to reach it in time) or should I secrete it in your violin (but would you notice it there)?

'In this mental dilemma I allowed the muscles of my jaw to relax, the hansom gave a sudden lurch and, alas! I swallowed the Dark Diamond of Dungbura.'

'Impossible,' exclaimed Holmes, 'It is too large.'

'I have swallowed much in my time,' retorted Watson with quiet dignity. A new access of pain swept over him and his face contorted with agony.

'How he suffers,' cried Holmes, 'it is a tortured brain.'

'No, no. Alimentary, my dear Holmes, alimentary,' gasped Watson. 'Take me to a hospital and I will stake my medical reputation that the Dark Diamond can speedily be recovered.'

Holmes drew me aside.

'Watson,' he said, 'has bungled shamefully, as I fear he often does—nevertheless we might still use some part of his strange plan. I could well restore the diamond to Great Cumberland Place.'

It was then that I took command of the situation.

'No, Mr Holmes,' said I, 'that is out of the question. When the Yard undertakes a case of this kind it does not rest until success is achieved. Within twenty-four hours of taking over the case I have laid my hands on the criminal, who now writhes in your chair, and I have—within very narrow limits—located the stolen diamond. With some assistance from the hospital I shall recover it and I shall restore it to its owner.'

But I noted a look of chagrin on Holmes' face, so I tapped him on the shoulder and tried to console him.

'The Yard,' I said, 'cares little to whom the credit goes if only its task is achieved. After all, the confession which I extracted from Dr Watson has saved me some hours of patient investigation; if, therefore, Mr Wimpfheimer recovers I shall inform him that the Gifted Amateur Mr Sherlock Holmes lent his assistance to us in the recovery of the diamond.'

A happy smile passed over the great Lestrade's wrinkled face.

'I am not denying,' he said, 'that my speed and efficiency in the handling of the case of the Dark Diamond was a big step upward in my professional career.

GIFTED AMATEUR

'Nor did I forget my promise to the Gifted Amateur. Mr
Rheinhart Wimpfheimer recovered and when, some three or
four months later, I met Mr Sherlock Holmes, he was wearing a
handsome diamond tiepin which I do not remember to have
seen in his possession before.'

99

→ ❋ 11 ❋ ←

GAVIN BREND

THE ROUTE OF THE BLUE CARBUNCLE

On December 22nd in a year which most of us believe to be 1889 the blue carbuncle vanished from the Hotel Cosmopolitan. There is no positive evidence that it ever returned there, and the last view we have of the 'pretty toy' discloses Holmes placing it in his strong-box at 221B. He was however about to write to the Countess of Morcar reporting the discovery and I think that she would still be at the Cosmopolitan. She may have only been there on a temporary visit, but even if the time for her departure had come she would be delayed by the forthcoming proceedings in the police court against Horner. Aesthetically speaking, I like the idea of the carbuncle beginning and ending its journey at the same place and I shall therefore assume that this is what actually happened.

Such being the case, the object of this essay is to trace its route from start to finish. It is not a subject on which I have passionate convictions. What follows is put forward in a tentative and experimental manner in the hope that it will start up rival theories and thus create a new Sherlockian controversy. This is merely the Brend Route.

As I see it, the carbuncle was carried round London by a relay team of six people, of whom only the first and last knew what they were carrying. Speaking very roughly, the course is triangular in shape with the first and sixth carriers heading south, the second and third north and the fourth and fifth west. The successive carriers were James Ryder, Breckinridge, Bill (surname unknown), Henry Baker, Peterson and the Countess of Morcar. In addition to these there is a sort of reserve team consisting of Mrs Oakshott, Windigate, Mrs Peterson and

Holmes who successively have the jewel in their possession though they do not actively assist it on its journey.

The following is the route, with the streets bearing their present names which were not necessarily the same in 1889. I have put in the time that it takes to walk each stage although several of the carriers did not in fact travel on foot.

First Stage. James Ryder. One hour
Claridges, Brook Street, Avery Row, Bond Street, St James's Street, St James's Park, Queen Anne's Gate, Broadway, Tothill Street, Deans Yard, Great College Street, Millbank, Lambeth Bridge, Albert Embankment, Harleyford Street, the Oval, Brixton Road to No. 117.

Second Stage. Mr Breckinridge. 48 minutes
Brixton Road, Kennington Park Road, Elephant, St George's Circus, Waterloo Bridge, Wellington Street, Russell Street, Covent Garden to his shop.

Third Stage. Bill. 9 minutes
James Street, Neal Street, Shorts Gardens, Endell Street, Grape Street, Coptic Street, Little Russell Street to the Plough.

Fourth Stage. Henry Baker. 8 minutes
Museum Street, Great Russell Street, Tottenham Court Road to Goodge Street.

Fifth Stage. Peterson. 19 minutes
Tottenham Court Road, Howland Street, New Cavendish Street, Blandford Street, Baker Street to 221B.

Sixth Stage. The Countess of Morcar. 11 minutes
Baker Street, Orchard Street, Oxford Street, Davies Street to Claridges.

I take the Cosmopolitan to be Claridges. There are no doubt some other possible selections, but I believe they are fewer than might be supposed. The Ritz, the Carlton, the Berkeley and the Cecil all came into existence after 1889 though some of them were built on the sites of earlier hotels. The Savoy opened in October of that year but it is unlikely (I hope) that within a couple of months a bedroom grate would already be in need of repair.

The first and longest stage of the journey is made by Ryder

and he covers the whole of it on foot. Any conveyance seems to be ruled out by his statement 'all the way there every man I met seemed to be a policeman or a detective and for all that it was a cold night, the sweat was pouring down my face before I came to the Brixton Road'. We know that when he discovered what had happened he 'ran off as hard as [his] feet would carry [him] to this man Breckinridge'. From this I conclude that he was never able to afford any more comfortable form of transport and that probably even the intervening journey in which he carried the wrong goose from Brixton to Kilburn would be made on foot.

I must admit that I have a sort of sneaking sympathy for Ryder in spite of his somewhat unattractive character. I have always imagined him as a lonely, impoverished type who probably spent all his spare time in visiting his sister, Maggie Oakshott, who obviously spoiled him, as witness the retention of the largest goose for his disposal. If these journeys were always made on foot I think he would learn to take the shortest course and I have therefore tried to save his shoe leather by making him take what appears to me to be the most direct route for a pedestrian from Claridges to the Brixton Road.

Let us pause for a minute at Mrs Oakshott's residence, No. 117 Brixton Road, and remember that we are back in the year 1889. Suppose in its efforts to escape from Ryder the goose had scrambled over the north garden wall of No. 117, where do you imagine that it would be? The answer is—believe it or not —that it would be in Baker Street! No. 117 stands at the corner of Brixton Road and a side street which since 1937 has been called Blackwell Street but which before that bore the name of Baker Street. If we were dealing with a work of fiction we might wonder whether this was a mere coincidence or whether the author selected 117 Brixton Road as a private joke of his own simply because he knew that it was adjacent to Baker Street, Brixton.

We can now return to the second stage of our journey. Was the second carrier someone from Brixton Road or someone from Covent Garden? I favour the latter alternative on the somewhat slender grounds that when Maggie is asked where the geese are, she merely replies, 'Gone to the dealers.' I suggest that this is too impersonal. After all conveying two dozen geese (even if they are dead ones) across London is quite an undertaking and I think that if she or anyone else in her establishment had taken them this fact would have been mentioned.

If someone from Covent Garden called to collect them, there can be little doubt that this would be Mr Breckinridge in person. He impresses me as being a very businesslike character and I think he would want to inspect his purchases in person before buying. He would collect them in a cart and if he really does live in Covent Garden there seems to be no particular reason why he should depart from the main road via Kennington, the Elephant and Waterloo.

But does he live in Covent Garden? At this stage in the argument I anticipate a breakaway from my party by a rival group under the very able leadership of Mr Ian M. Leslie who pointed out in an earlier number of the *Journal* that Covent Garden then, as now, was a fruit and vegetable market and not a poultry market. Watson, probably as the result of some 'small jollification' the night before, had confused Covent Garden with Leadenhall Street. For myself, I feel that my journey is already quite long enough without the addition of Leadenhall Street, so waving farewell to Mr Leslie at the Elephant as he heads towards the City, I continue on my course to Covent Garden, passing on the way the Lyceum with its 'third pillar from the left', the scene of a famous rendezvous in *The Sign of Four*.

Mr Breckinridge's cart will be required again for the third stage of the journey, for we cannot expect Mr Windigate of the 'Alpha' to have the facilities for collecting twenty-four geese. This time, however, there is no need for Mr Breckinridge's personal attendance. It will be quite sufficient if one of his assistants delivers the birds. Allow me to introduce you to Bill.

I have a feeling that you may have forgotten Bill or overlooked him, since he is very small and he only makes two brief appearances in the narrative, first when he helps Breckinridge to put up the shutters and secondly when he hands him the books. We only knew him as 'Bill'. Whether or not his surname is 'Breckinridge' is one of the many problems to which I hope the Sherlock Holmes Society will supply the answer in the near future.

I expect Mr Breckinridge had many assistants since he was

able to assure Holmes that he could have 500 birds on the following day, but from them all I shall select Bill on the principle of 'Better the devil you know than the devil you don't know.' I have made him take in as many small side streets as possible so as to harmonize with the journey made by Holmes and Watson in the reverse direction.

We are now at the 'Alpha' which Mr Christopher Morley identified as the 'Museum' Tavern opposite the gates of the British Museum. This is a very nice pub whose hospitality I have frequently enjoyed, but my own preference is for the 'Plough' at the corner of Museum and Little Russell Streets on the grounds that Alpha is the largest star in the constellation of the Plough.

On coming out of the 'Plough' into Little Russell Street, Henry Baker's most direct course is to turn to the right, but I have routed him to the left back into Museum Street and past the 'Museum' Tavern so as to keep in step with Mr Morley. I do not think Henry will object to the slight extra distance. By now he is past objecting to anything. It is four o'clock in the morning and it has been a really good party.

Peterson takes over from Henry at the corner of Tottenham Court Road and Goodge Street. This sounds definite enough, yet even here there is room for argument. Was it the north corner or the south? I choose the south. Henry is clearly proceeding northwards along Tottenham Court Road. Now, if the roughs are coming out of Goodge Street on the south side, neither party will see the other until they run into each other on the south corner. On the other hand if the collision occurs on the north corner, no matter from what direction the roughs approach each party is visible to the other and has an opportunity of avoiding the other if so desired. It is possible that both parties were in a belligerent mood and that neither made any attempt to avoid the crash. Yet I would like to think that the original cause was accidental. After all it was 'the season of forgiveness' and I would like to reduce all unpleasantness to a minimum even in this unfortunate business of Henry Baker and the roughs.

I am assuming that Peterson lived at 221B though I am not sure that this is correct. Holmes gives him orders to carry out and he rushes into the room unannounced when his wife discovers the carbuncle. It looks as if he lived there. Yet the more I consider the domestic and service side of 221B, the less am I inclined to be dogmatic.

All the same I have routed Peterson for 221B and have made him take the most suitable road for those who believe (as I do) that 221B lies in that part of Baker Street which is between Blandford Street and Dorset Street. Here again there will obviously be a breakaway. This time the party will be led by Mr J. E. Holroyd and it will deviate slightly to the north so as to reach Camden House.

All that now remains is to get the carbuncle from 221B to Claridges. Apparently Holmes was not prepared to run the risk of sending it to the Countess by registered post. I surmise that he was afraid that that attractive but predatory creature, Catherine Cusack, might have another chance of getting her dainty hands upon it. Did Holmes himself take it to Claridges? I think not. He was never the man to stand any nonsense from the aristocracy (or anyone else) and I think he made the Countess come to Baker Street to collect her 'pretty toy'. Her carriage would probably follow the main roads both going and returning.

That completes my route which runs through five London boroughs. I have covered the distance in 2 hours 35 minutes which I think I can reasonably claim as a world's record since it is virtually certain that no human being has ever before walked this walk in its entirety.

12

ADRIAN CONAN DOYLE

THE ADVENTURE OF THE DEPTFORD HORROR

I have remarked elsewhere that my friend Sherlock Holmes, like all great artists, lived for his art's sake and, save in the case of the Duke of Holdernesse, I have seldom known him claim any substantial reward. However powerful or wealthy the client, he would refuse to undertake any problem that lacked appeal to his sympathies, while he would devote his most intense energies to the affairs of some humble person whose case contained those singular and remarkable qualities which struck a responsive chord in his imagination.

On glancing through my notes for that memorable year '95, I find recorded the details of a case which may be taken as a typical instance of this disinterested and even altruistic attitude of mind which placed the rendering of a kindly service above that of material reward. I refer, of course, to the dreadful affair of the canaries and the soot-marks on the ceiling.

It was early in June that my friend completed his investigations into the sudden death of Cardinal Tosca, an inquiry which he had undertaken at the special request of the Pope. The case had demanded the most exacting work on Holmes' part and, as I had feared at the time, the aftermath had left him in a highly nervous and restless state that caused me some concern both as his friend and his medical adviser.

One rainy night towards the end of the same month, I persuaded him to dine with me at Frascati's and thereafter we had gone on to the Café Royal for our coffee and liqueurs. As I had hoped, the bustle of the great room, with its red plush seats and stately palms bathed in the glow of numerous crystal chandeliers, drew him out of his introspective mood and as he leaned back on our sofa, his fingers playing with the stem of his

106

glass, I noted with satisfaction a gleam of interest in those keen grey eyes as he studied the somewhat Bohemian clientele that thronged the tables and alcoves.

I was in the act of replying to some remark when Holmes nodded suddenly in the direction of the door.

'Lestrade,' said he. 'What can he be doing here?'

Glancing over my shoulder, I saw the lean, rat-faced figure of the Scotland Yard man standing in the entrance, his dark eyes roving slowly around the room.

'He may be seeking you,' I remarked. 'Probably on some urgent case.'

'Hardly, Watson. His wet boots show that he has walked. If there was urgency, he would have taken a cab. But here he comes.'

The police agent had caught sight of us and, at Holmes' gesture, he pushed his way through the throng and drew up a chair to the table.

'Only a routine check,' said he, in reply to my friend's query. 'But duty's duty, Mr Holmes, and I can tell you that I've netted some strange fish before now in these respectable places. While you are comfortably dreaming up your theories in Baker Street, we poor devils at Scotland Yard are doing the practical work. No thanks to us from Popes and Kings but a bad hour on the Superintendent's carpet if we fail.'

'Tut,' smiled Holmes good-humouredly. 'Your superiors must surely hold you in some esteem since I solved the Ronald Adair murder, the Bruce-Partington theft, the—'

'Quite so, quite so,' interrupted Lestrade hurriedly. 'And now,' he added, with a heavy wink at me, 'I have something for you.'

'Ah!'

'Of course, a young woman who starts at shadows may be more in Dr Watson's line.'

'Really, Lestrade,' I protested warmly, 'I cannot approve your—'

'One moment, Watson. Let us hear the facts.'

'Well, Mr Holmes, they are absurd enough,' continued Lestrade, 'and I would not waste your time were it not that I have known you to do a kindness or two before now and your word of advice may in this instance prevent a young woman from acting foolishly. Now, here's the position.

'Down Deptford way, along the edge of the river, there are some of the worst slums in the East End of London but, right in the middle of them, you can still find some fine old houses which were once the homes of wealthy merchants centuries ago. One of these tumbledown mansions has been occupied by a family named Wilson for the past hundred years and more. I understand that they were originally in the China trade and when that went to the dogs a generation back, they got out in time and remained on in the old home. The recent household consisted of Horatio Wilson and his wife, with one son and a daughter, and Horatio's younger brother, Theobold, who had gone to live with them on his return from foreign parts.

'Some three years ago, the body of Horatio Wilson was hooked out of the river. He had been drowned and, as he was known to have been a hard-drinking man, it was generally accepted that he had missed his step in the fog and fallen into the water. A year later, his wife, who suffered from a weak heart, died from a heart attack. We know this to be the case, because the doctor made a very careful examination following the statements of a police-constable and a night-watchman employed on a Thames barge.'

'Statements to what effect?' interposed Holmes.

'Well, there was talk of some noise rising apparently from the old Wilson house. But the nights are often foggy along Thames-side and the men were probably misled. The constable described the sound as a dreadful yell that froze the blood in his veins. If I had him in my division, I'd teach him that such words should never pass the lips of an officer of the law.'

'What time was this?'

'Ten o'clock at night, the hour of the old lady's death. It's merely a coincidence, for there is no doubt that she died of heart.'

'Go on.'

Lestrade consulted his note-book for a moment. 'I've been digging up the facts,' he continued. 'On the night of May 17th last, the daughter went to a magic-lantern entertainment accompanied by a woman servant. On her return, she found her brother, Phineas Wilson, dead in his arm-chair. He had inherited a bad heart and insomnia from his mother. This time there were no rumours of shrieks and yells, but owing to the expression on the dead man's face, the local doctor called in the police-surgeon to assist in the examination. It was heart, all right, and our man confirmed that this can sometimes cause a distortion of the features that will convey an impression of stark terror.'

'That is perfectly true,' I remarked.

'Now it seems that the daughter Janet has become so over-wrought that, according to her uncle, she proposes to sell up the property and go abroad,' went on Lestrade. 'Her feelings are, I suppose, natural. Death has been busy with the Wilson family.'

'And what of this uncle? Theobold, I think you said his name was.'

'Well, I fancy that you will find him on your doorstep to-morrow morning. He came to me at the Yard in the hope that the official police could put his niece's fears at rest and per-suade her to take a more reasonable view. As we are engaged on more important affairs than calming hysterical young women, I advised him to call on you.'

'Indeed! Well, it is natural enough that he should resent the unnecessary loss of what is probably a snug corner.'

'There is no resentment, Mr Holmes. Wilson seems to be genuinely attached to his niece and concerned only for her future.' Lestrade paused, while a grin spread over his foxy face. 'He is not a very worldly person, is Mr Theobold, and though I've met some queer trades in my time his beats the band. The man trains canaries.'

'It is an established profession.'

'Is it?' There was an irritating smugness in Lestrade's manner as he rose to his feet and reached for his hat. 'It is quite evident that you do not suffer from insomnia, Mr Holmes,' said he, 'or you would know that birds trained by Theobold Wilson are different from other canaries. Good night, gentlemen.'

'What on earth does the fellow mean?' I asked, as the police-agent threaded his way towards the door.

'Merely that he knows something that we do not,' replied Holmes drily. 'But, as conjecture is as profitless as it is mis-leading to the analytical mind, let us wait until tomorrow. I can say, however, that I do not propose to waste my time over a matter that appears to fall more properly within the province of the local vicar.'

To my friend's relief, the morning brought no visitor. But when, on my return from an urgent case to which I had been summoned shortly after lunch, I entered our sitting-room, I found that our spare chair was occupied by a bespectacled middle-aged man. As he rose to his feet, I observed that he was of an exceeding thinness and that his face, which was scholarly and even austere in expression, was seamed with countless wrinkles and of that dull parchment-yellow that comes from years under a tropic sun.

'Ah, Watson, you have arrived just in time,' said Holmes. 'This is Mr Theobold Wilson about whom Lestrade spoke to us last night.'

Our visitor wrung my hand warmly. 'Your name is, of course, well known to me, Dr Watson,' he cried. 'Indeed, if Mr Sherlock Holmes will pardon me for saying so, it is largely thanks to you that we are aware of his genius. As a medical man doubtless well versed in the handling of nervous cases, your presence should have a most beneficial effect upon my unhappy niece.'

Holmes caught my eye resignedly. 'I have promised Mr Wilson to accompany him to Deptford, Watson,' said he, 'for it would seem that the young lady is determined to leave her home tomorrow. But I must repeat again, Mr Wilson, that I fail to see in what way my presence can affect the matter.'

'You are over-modest, Mr Holmes. When I appealed to the official police, I had hoped that they might convince Janet that, terrible though our family losses have been in the past three years, nevertheless they lay in natural causes and that there is no reason why she should flee from her home. I had the impression,' he added, with a chuckle, 'that the inspector was somewhat chagrined at my ready acceptance of his own suggestion that I should invoke your assistance.'

'I shall certainly remember my small debt to Lestrade,' replied Holmes drily as he rose to his feet. 'Perhaps, Watson, you would ask Mrs Hudson to whistle a four-wheeler and Mr Wilson can clarify certain points to my mind as we drive to Deptford.'

It was one of those grey, brooding summer days when London is at its worst and, as we rattled over Blackfriars Bridge, I noted that wreaths of mist were rising from the river like the poisonous vapours of some hot jungle swamp. The more spacious streets of the West End had given place to the great commercial thoroughfares, resounding with the stamp and clatter of the dray-horses, and these in turn merged at last into a maze of dingy streets that, following the curve of the river, grew more and more wretched in their squalor the nearer we approached to that labyrinth of tidal basins and dark, evil-smelling lanes that were once the ancient cradle of England's sea trade and of an empire's wealth. I could see that Holmes was listless and bored to a point of irritation and I did my best, therefore, to engage our companion in conversation.

'I understand that you are an expert on canaries,' I remarked.

Theobold Wilson's eyes, behind their powerful spectacles, lit with the glow of the enthusiast. 'A mere student, sir, but with thirty years of practical research,' he cried. 'Can it be that you too—? No? A pity! The study, breeding and training of the *Fringilla Canaria* is a task worthy of a man's lifetime. You would not credit the ignorance, Dr Watson, that prevails on this subject even in the most enlightened circles. When I read my paper on the "Crossing of the Madeira and Canary Island Strains" to the British Ornithological Society I was appalled at the puerility of the ensuing questions.'

'Inspector Lestrade hinted at some special characteristic in your training of these little songsters.'

'Songsters, sir! A thrush is a songster. The *Fringilla* is the supreme ear of Nature, possessing a unique power of imitation which can be trained for the benefit and edification of the human race. But the inspector was correct,' he went on more calmly, 'in that I have put my birds to a special effect. They are trained to sing by night in artificial light.'

'Surely a somewhat singular pursuit.'

'I like to think that it is a kindly one. My birds are trained for the benefit of those who suffer from insomnia and I have clients in all parts of the country. Their tuneful song helps to while away the long night hours and the dousing of the lamplight terminates the concert.'

'It seems to me that Lestrade was right,' I observed. 'Yours is indeed a unique profession.'

During our conversation, Holmes, who had idly picked up our companion's heavy stick, had been examining it with some attention.

'I understand that you returned to England some three years ago,' he observed.

'I did.'

'From Cuba, I perceive.'

Theobold Wilson started and for an instant I seemed to catch a gleam of something like wariness in the swift glance that he shot at Holmes.

'That is so,' he said. 'But how did you know?'

'Your stick is cut from Cuban ebony. There is no mistaking that greenish tint and the exceptionally high polish.'

'It might have been bought in London since my return from, say, Africa.'

'No, it has been yours for some years.' Holmes lifted the stick to the carriage-window and tilted it so that the daylight shone upon the handle. 'You will perceive,' he went on, 'that there is a slight but regular scraping that has worn through the polish along the left side of the handle just where the ring finger of a left-handed man would close upon the grip. Ebony is among the toughest of woods and it would require considerable time to cause such wear and a ring of some harder metal than gold. You are left-handed, Mr Wilson, and wear a silver ring on your middle finger.'

'Dear me, how simple. I thought for the moment that you had done something clever. As it happens, I was in the sugar trade in Cuba and brought my old stick back with me. But here we are at the house, and if you can put my silly niece's fears at rest as quickly as you can deduce my past, I shall be your debtor, Mr Sherlock Holmes.'

On descending from our four-wheeler, we found ourselves in a lane of mean, slatternly houses sloping, so far as I could judge from the yellow mist that was already creeping up the lower end, to the river's edge. At one side was a high wall of crumbling brickwork pierced by an iron gate through which we caught a glimpse of a substantial mansion lying in its own garden.

'The old house has known better days,' said our companion, as we followed him through the gate and up the path. 'It was built in the year that Peter the Great came to live in Scales Court, whose ruined park can be seen from the upper windows.'

Usually I am not unduly affected by my surroundings, but I must confess that I was aware of a feeling of depression at the melancholy spectacle that lay before us. The house, though of dignified and even imposing proportions, was faced with blotched, weatherstained plaster which had fallen away in places to disclose the ancient brickwork that lay beneath, while a tangled mass of ivy covering one wall had sent its long tendrils across the high-peaked roof to wreathe itself around the chimneystacks.

The garden was an overgrown wilderness, and the air of the whole place reeked with the damp musty smell of the river.

Theobold Wilson led us through a small hall into a comfortably furnished drawing-room. A young woman with auburn hair and a freckled face, who was sorting through some papers at a writing-desk, sprang to her feet at our entrance.

'Here are Mr Sherlock Holmes and Dr Watson,' announced our companion. 'This is my niece Janet, whose interests you are here to protect against her own unreasonable conduct.'

The young lady faced us bravely enough, though I noted a twitch and tremor of the lips that spoke of a high nervous tension. 'I am leaving tomorrow, Uncle,' she cried, 'and nothing that these gentlemen can say will alter my decision. Here, there is only sorrow and fear—above all, fear!'

'Fear of what?'

The girl passed her hand over her eyes. 'I—I cannot explain. I hate the shadows and the funny little noises.'

'You have inherited both money and property, Janet,' said Mr Wilson earnestly. 'Will you, because of shadows, desert the roof of your fathers? Be reasonable.'

'We are here only to serve you, young lady,' said Holmes with some gentleness, 'and to try to put your fears at rest. It is often so in life that we injure our own best interests by precipitate action.'

'You will laugh at a woman's intuitions, sir.'

'By no means. They are often the signposts of Providence. Understand clearly that you will go or stay as you see fit. But perhaps, as I am here, it might relieve your mind to show me over the house.'

'An admirable suggestion!' cried Theobold Wilson cheerily. 'Come, Janet, we will soon dispose of your shadows and noises.'

In a little procession, we trooped from one over-furnished room to another on the ground floor.

'I will take you to the bedrooms,' said Miss Wilson, as we paused at last before the staircase.

'Are there no cellars in a house of this antiquity?'

'There is one cellar, Mr Holmes, but it is little used save for the storage of wood and some of Uncle's old nest-boxes. This way, please.'

It was a gloomy, stone-built chamber in which we found ourselves. A stack of wood was piled against one wall and a pot-bellied Dutch stove, its iron pipe running through the ceiling, filled the far corner. Through a glazed door reached by a line of steps and opening into the garden, a dim light filtered down upon the flagstones. Holmes sniffed the air keenly, and I was myself aware of an increased mustiness from the nearby river.

'Like most Thames-side houses, you must be plagued by rats,' he remarked.

'We used to be. But, since Uncle came here, he has got rid of them.'

'Quite so. Dear me,' he continued, peering down at the floor, 'what busy little fellows!'

Following his gaze, I saw that his attention had been drawn by a few garden ants scurrying across the floor from beneath the edge of the stove and up the steps leading to the garden door. 'It is as well for us, Watson,' he chuckled, pointing with his stick at the tiny particles with which they were encumbered, 'that we are not under the necessity of lugging along our dinners thrice our own size. It is a lesson in patience.' He lapsed into silence, staring thoughtfully at the floor. 'A lesson,' he repeated slowly.

Mr Wilson's thin lips tightened. 'What foolery is this,' he exclaimed. 'The ants are there because the servants would throw garbage in the stove to save themselves the trouble of going to the dustbin.'

'And so you put a lock on the lid.'

'We did. If you wish, I can fetch the key. No? Then, if you are finished, let me take you to the bedrooms.'

'Perhaps I may see the room where your brother died,' requested Holmes, as we reached the top floor.

'It is here,' replied Miss Wilson, throwing open the door.

It was a large chamber furnished with some taste and even luxury and lit by two deeply recessed windows flanking another pot-bellied stove decorated with yellow tiles to harmonize with the tone of the room. A pair of bird-cages hung from the stove-pipe.

'Where does that side door lead?' asked my friend.

'It communicates with my room, which was formerly used by my mother,' she answered.

For a few minutes, Holmes prowled around listlessly.

'I perceive that your brother was addicted to night reading,' he remarked.

'Yes. He suffered from sleeplessness. But how—'

'Tut, the pile of the carpet on the right of the armchair is thick with traces of candle-wax. But hullo! What have we here?'

Holmes had halted near the window and was staring intently at the upper wall. Then, mounting the sill, he stretched out an arm and, touching the plaster lightly here and there, sniffed at his finger-tips. There was a puzzled frown on his face as he clambered down and commenced to circle slowly around the room, his eyes fixed upon the ceiling.

'Most singular,' he muttered.

'Is anything wrong, Mr Holmes?' faltered Miss Wilson.

'I am merely interested to account for these odd whorls and lines across the upper wall and plaster.'

'It must be those dratted cockroaches dragging the dust all over the place,' exclaimed Wilson apologetically. 'I've told you before, Janet, that you would be better employed in supervising the servants' work. But what now, Mr Holmes?'

My friend, who had crossed to the side door and glanced within, now closed it again and strolled across to the window.

'My visit has been a useless one,' said he, 'and, as I see that the fog is rising, I fear that we must take our leave. These are, I suppose, your famous canaries?' he added, pointing to the cages above the stove.

'A mere sample. But come this way.'

Wilson led us along the passage and threw open a door.

'There!' said he.

Obviously it was his own bedroom and yet unlike any bedroom that I had entered in all my professional career. From floor to ceiling it was festooned with scores of cages and the little golden-coated singers within filled the air with their sweet warbling and trilling.

'Daylight or lamplight, it's all the same to them. Here, Carrie, Carrie!' he whistled a few liquid notes which I seemed to recognize. The bird took them up into a lovely cadence of song.

'A sky-lark!' I cried.

'Precisely. As I said before, the *Fringilla* if properly trained are the supreme imitators.'

'I confess that I do not recognize that song,' I remarked, as one of the birds broke into a low rising, whistle ending in a curious *tremolo*.

Mr Wilson threw a towel over the cage. 'It is the song of a tropic night-bird,' he said shortly, 'and, as I have the foolish pride to prefer my birds to sing the songs of the day while it is day, we will punish Peperino by putting him in darkness.'

'I am surprised that you prefer an open fireplace here to a stove,' observed Holmes. 'There must be a considerable draught.'

'I have not noticed one. Dear me, the fog is indeed increasing. I am afraid, Mr Holmes, that you have a bad journey before you.'

'Then we must be on our way.'

As we descended the stairs and paused in the hall while Theobold Wilson fetched our hats, Sherlock Holmes leaned over towards our young companion.

'I would remind you, Miss Wilson, of what I said earlier about a woman's intuition,' he said quietly. 'There are occasions when the truth can be sensed more easily than it can be seen. Goodnight.'

A moment later, we were feeling our way down the garden path to where the lights of our waiting four-wheeler shone dimly through the rising fog.

My companion was sunk in thought as we rumbled westward through the mean streets whose squalor was the more aggressive under the garish light of the gaslamps that flared and whistled outside the numerous public houses. The night promised to be a bad one and already, through the yellow vapour thickening and writhing above the pavements, the occasional wayfarer was nothing more than a vague hurrying shadow.

'I could have wished, my dear fellow,' I remarked, 'that you had been spared the need uselessly to waste your energies which are already sufficiently depleted.'

'Well, well, Watson. I fancied that the affairs of the Wilson family would prove no concern of ours. And yet—' he sank back, absorbed for a moment in his own thoughts, '—and yet, it is wrong, wrong, all wrong!' I heard him mutter under his breath.

'I observed nothing of a sinister nature.'

'Nor I. But every danger bell in my head is jangling its warning. Why a fireplace, Watson, why a fireplace? I take it that you noticed that the pipe from the cellar connected with the stoves in the other bedrooms?'

'In one bedroom.'

'No. There was the same arrangement in the adjoining room where the mother died.'

'I see nothing in this save an old-fashioned system of heating flues.'

'And what of the marks on the ceiling?'

'You mean the whorls of dust.'

'I mean the whorls of soot.'

'Soot! Surely you are mistaken, Holmes.'

'I touched them, smelt them, examined them. They were speckles and lines of wood-soot.'

'Well, there is probably some perfectly natural explanation.'

For a time, we sat in silence. Our cab had reached the beginnings of the City and I was gazing out of the window, my fingers drumming idly on the half-lowered pane, which was already befogged with moisture, when my thoughts were recalled by a sharp ejaculation from my companion. He was staring fixedly over my shoulder.

'The glass,' he muttered.

Over the clouded surface there now lay an intricate tracery of whorls and lines where my finger had wandered aimlessly.

Holmes clapped his hand to his brow and, throwing open the other window, he shouted an order to the cabby. The vehicle turned in its tracks and, with the driver lashing at his horse, we clattered away into the thickening gloom.

'Ah, Watson, Watson, true it is that none are so blind as those who will not see!' quoted Holmes bitterly, sinking back into his corner. 'All the facts were there, staring me in the face, and yet logic failed to respond.'

'What facts?'

'There are nine. Four alone should have sufficed. Here is a man from Cuba, who not only trains canaries in a singular manner but knows the call of tropical night-birds and keeps a fireplace in his bedroom. There is devilry here, Watson. Stop, cabby, stop!'

We were passing a junction of two busy thoroughfares, with the golden balls of a pawnshop glimmering above a street-lamp. Holmes sprang out. But after a few minutes, he was back again and we recommenced our journey.

'It is fortunate that we are still in the City,' he chuckled, 'for I fancy that the East End pawnshops are unlikely to run to golf-clubs.'

'Good heavens—!' I began, only to lapse into silence while I stared down at the heavy niblick which he had thrust into my hand. The first shadows of some vague and monstrous horror seemed to rise up and creep over my mind.

'We are too early,' exclaimed Holmes, consulting his watch. 'A sandwich and a glass of whisky at the first public house will not come amiss.'

The clock on St Nicholas Church was striking ten when we found ourselves once again in that evil-smelling garden. Through the mist, the dark gloom of the house was broken by a single feeble light in an upper window. 'It is Miss Wilson's room,' said Holmes. 'Let us hope that this handful of gravel will rouse her without alarming the household.'

An instant later, there came the sound of an opening window.

'Who is there?' demanded a tremulous voice.

'It is Sherlock Holmes,' my friend called back softly. 'I must speak with you at once, Miss Wilson. Is there a side door?'

'There is one in the wall to your left. But what has happened?'

'Pray descend immediately. Not a word to your uncle.'

We felt our way along the wall and reached the door just as it opened to disclose Miss Wilson. She was in her dressing-gown, her hair tumbled about her shoulders and, as her startled eyes peered at us across the light of the candle in her hand, the shadows danced and trembled on the wall behind her.

'What is it, Mr Holmes?' she gasped.

'All will be well, if you carry out my instructions,' my friend replied quietly. 'Where is your uncle?'

'He is in his room.'

'Good. While Dr Watson and I occupy your room, you will move into your late brother's bedchamber. If you value your life,' he added solemnly, 'you will not attempt to leave it.'

'You frighten me!' she whimpered.

'Rest assured that we will take care of you. And now two final questions before you retire. Has your uncle visited you this evening?'

'Yes. He brought Peperino and put him with the other birds in the cage in my room. He said that as it was my last night at home I should have the best entertainment that he had the power to give me.'

'Ha! Quite so. Your last night. Tell me, Miss Wilson, do you suffer at all from the same malady as your mother and brother?'

'A weak heart? I must confess it, yes.'

'Well, we will accompany you quietly upstairs where you will retire to the adjoining room. Come, Watson.'

Guided by the light of Janet Wilson's candle, we mounted silently to the floor above and thence into the bedchamber which Holmes had previously examined. While we waited for our companion to collect her things from the adjoining room, Holmes strolled across and, lifting the edge of the cloths which now covered the two bird-cages, peered in at the tiny sleeping occupants.

'The evil of man is as inventive as it is immeasurable,' said he, and I noticed that his face was very stern.

On Miss Wilson's return, having seen that she was safely ensconced for the night, I followed Holmes into the room which she had lately occupied. It was a small chamber but comfortably furnished and lit by a heavy silver oil-lamp. Immediately above a tiled Dutch stove there hung a cage containing three canaries which, momentarily ceasing their song, cocked their little golden heads at our approach.

'I think, Watson, that it would be as well to relax for half an hour,' whispered Holmes as we sank into our chairs. 'So kindly put out the light.'

'But, my dear fellow, if there is any danger it would be an act of madness!' I protested.

'There is no danger in the darkness.'

'Would it not be better,' I said severely, 'that you were frank with me? You have made it obvious that the birds are being put to some evil purpose, but what is this danger that exists only in the lamplight?'

'I have my own ideas on that matter, Watson, but it is better that we should wait and see. I would draw your attention, however, to the hinged lid of the stoke-hole on the top of the stove.'

'It appears to be a perfectly normal fitting.'

'Just so. But is there not some significance in the fact that the stoke-hole of an iron stove should be fitted with a tin lid?'

'Great heavens, Holmes!' I cried, as the light of understanding burst upon me. 'You mean that this man Wilson has used the inter-connecting pipes from the stove in the cellar to those in the bedrooms to disseminate some deadly poison to wipe out his own kith and kin and thus obtain the property. It is for that reason that he has a fireplace in his own bedroom. I see it all.'

'Well, you are not far wrong, Watson, though I fancy that Master Theobold is rather more subtle than you suppose. He possesses the two qualities vital to the successful murderer—ruthlessness and imagination. But now, douse the light like a good fellow and for a while let us relax. If my reading of the problem is correct, our nerves may be tested to their limit before we see tomorrow's dawn.'

I lay back in the darkness and drawing some comfort from the thought that ever since the affair with Colonel Sebastian Moran I had carried my revolver in my pocket, I sought in my mind for some explanation that would account for the warning contained in Holmes' words. But I must have been wearier than I had imagined. My thoughts grew more and more confused and finally I dozed off.

It was a touch upon my arm that awoke me. The lamp had been relit and my friend was bending over me, his long black shadow thrown upon the ceiling.

'Sorry to disturb you, Watson,' he whispered. 'But duty calls.'

'What do you wish me to do?'

'Sit still and listen. Peperino is singing.'

It was a vigil that I shall long remember. Holmes had tilted the lamp-shade, so that the light fell on the opposite wall broken by the window and the great tiled stove with its hanging bird-cage. The fog had thickened and the rays from the lamp, filtering through the window-glass, lost themselves in luminous clouds that swirled and boiled against the panes. My mind darkened by a premonition of evil, I would have found our surroundings melancholy enough without the eerie sound that was rising and falling from the canary cage. It was a kind of whistling beginning with a low, throaty warble and slowly ascending to a single chord that rang through the room like the note of a great wineglass, a sound so mesmeric in its repetition that almost imperceptibly the present seemed to melt away and my imagination to reach out beyond those fog-bound windows into the dark, lush depth of some exotic jungle. I had lost all count of time, and it was only the stillness following the sudden cessation of the bird's song that brought me back to reality. I glanced across the room and, in an instant, my heart gave one great throb and then seemed to stop beating altogether.

The lid of the stove was slowly rising.

My friends will agree that I am neither a nervous nor an impressionable man but I must confess that, as I sat there gripping the sides of my chair and glaring at the dreadful thing that was gradually clambering into view, my limbs momentarily refused their functions.

The lid had tilted back an inch or more and through the gap thus created a writhing mass of yellow, stick-like objects was clawing and scrabbling for a hold. And then, in a flash, it was out and standing motionless upon the surface of the stove.

Though I have always viewed with horror the bird-eating tarantulas of South America, they shrank into insignificance when compared with the loathsome creature that faced us now across that lamplit room. It was bigger in its spread than a large dinner-plate, with a hard, smooth, yellow body surrounded by legs that, rising high above it, conveyed a fearful impression that the thing was crouching for its spring. It was absolutely hairless save for tufts of stiff bristles around the leg-joints and, above the glint of its great poison mandibles, clusters of beady eyes shone in the light with a baleful red iridescence.

'Don't move, Watson,' whispered Holmes, and there was a note of horror in his voice that I had never heard before.

The sound roused the creature for, in a single lightning bound, it sprang from the stove to the top of the bird-cage and, reaching the wall, whizzed round the room and over the ceiling with a dreadful febrile swiftness that the eye could scarcely follow.

Holmes flung himself forward like a man possessed.

'Kill it! Smash it!' he yelled hoarsely, raining blow after blow with his golf-club at the blurred shape racing across the walls.

Dust from broken plaster choked the air and a table crashed over as I flung myself to the ground when the great spider cleared the room in a single leap and turned at bay. Holmes bounded across me, swinging his club. 'Keep where you are!' he shouted and even as his voice rang through the room, the thud . . . thud . . . thud of the blows was broken by a horrible squelching sound. For an instant, the creature hung there and then, slipping slowly down, it lay like a mess of smashed eggs with three thin, bony legs still twitching and plucking at the floor.

'Thank God that it missed you when it sprang!' I gasped, scrambling to my feet.

He made no reply and glancing up I caught a glimpse of his face reflected in a wall mirror. He looked pale and strained and there was a curious rigidity in his expression.

'I am afraid it's up to you, Watson,' he said quietly. 'It has a mate.'

I spun round to be greeted by a spectacle that I shall remember for the rest of my days. Sherlock Holmes was standing perfectly still within two feet of the stove and on top of it, reared up on its back legs, its loathsome body shuddering for the spring, stood another monstrous spider.

I knew instinctively that any sudden movement would merely precipitate the creature's leap and so, carefully drawing my revolver from my pocket, I fired point-blank.

Through the powder-smoke, I saw the thing shrink into itself and then, toppling slowly backwards, it fell through the open lid of the stove. There was a rasping, slithering sound rapidly fading away into silence.

'It's fallen down the pipe,' I cried, conscious that my hands were now shaking under a strong reaction. 'Are you all right, Holmes?'

He looked at me and there was a singular light in his eye.

'Thanks to you, my dear fellow!' he said soberly. 'If I had moved, then—but what is that?'

A door had slammed below and, an instant later, we caught the swift patter of feet upon the gravel path.

'After him!' cried Holmes, springing for the door. 'Your shot warned him that the game was up. He must not escape!'

But fate decreed otherwise. Though we rushed down the stairs and out into the fog, Theobold Wilson had too much start on us and the advantage of knowing the terrain. For a while, we followed the faint sound of his running footsteps down the empty lanes towards the river, but at length these died away in the distance.

'It is no good, Watson. We have lost our man,' panted Holmes. 'This is where the official police may be of use. But listen! Surely that was a cry?'

'I thought I heard something.'

'Well, it is hopeless to look further in the fog. Let us return and comfort this poor girl with the assurance that her troubles are now at an end.'

'They were nightmare creatures, Holmes,' I exclaimed, as we retraced our steps towards the house, 'and of some unknown species.'

'I think not, Watson,' said he. 'It was the *Galeodes* spider, the horror of the Cuban forests. It is perhaps fortunate for the rest of the world that it is found nowhere else. The creature is nocturnal in its habits and, unless my memory belies me, it possesses the power actually to break the spine of smaller creatures with a single blow of its mandibles. You will recall that Miss Janet mentioned that the rats had vanished since her uncle's return. Doubtless Wilson brought the brutes back with him,' he went on, 'and then conceived the idea of training certain of his canaries to imitate the song of some Cuban night-bird upon which the *Galeodes* were accustomed to feed. The marks on the ceiling were caused, of course, by the soot adhering to the spiders' legs after they had scrambled up the flues. It is fortunate, perhaps, for the consulting detective that the duster of the average housemaid seldom strays beyond the height of a mantelpiece.

'Indeed, I can discover no excuse for my lamentable slowness in solving this case, for the facts were before me from the first, and the whole affair was elementary in its construction.

'And yet to give Theobold Wilson his dues, one must recognize his almost diabolical cleverness. Once these horrors were installed in the stove in the cellar, what more simple than to arrange two ordinary flues communicating with the bedrooms above? By hanging the cages over the stoves, the flues would themselves act as a magnifier to the birds' song and, guided by their predatory instinct, the creatures would invariably ascend whichever pipe led to it. Once Wilson had devised some means of luring them back again to their nest, they represented a comparatively safe way of getting rid of those who stood between himself and the property.'

'Then its bite is deadly?' I interposed.

'To a person in weak health, probably so. But there lies the devilish cunning of the scheme, Watson. It was the sight of the thing rather than its bite, poisonous though it may be, on which he relied to kill his victim. Can you imagine the effect upon an elderly woman, and later upon her son, both suffering from insomnia and heart disease, when in the midst of a bird's seemingly innocent song this appalling spectacle arose from the top of the stove? We have sampled it ourselves, though we are healthy men. It killed them as surely as a bullet through their hearts.'

'There is one thing I cannot understand, Holmes. Why did he appeal to Scotland Yard?'

'Because he is a man of iron nerve. His niece was instinctively frightened and, finding that she was adamant in her intention of leaving, he planned to kill her at once and by the same method.

'Once done, who should dare to point the finger of suspicion at Master Theobold? Had he not appealed to Scotland Yard and even invoked the aid of Mr Sherlock Holmes himself to satisfy one and all? The girl had died of a heart attack like the others and her uncle would have been the recipient of general condolences.

'Remember the padlocked cover of the stove in the cellar

and admire the cold nerve that offered to fetch the key. It was bluff, of course, for he would have discovered that he had "lost" it. Had we persisted and forced that lock, I prefer not to think of what we would have found clinging round our collars.'

Theobold Wilson was never heard of again. But it is perhaps suggestive that, some two days later, a man's body was fished out of the Thames. The corpse was mutilated beyond recognition, probably by a ship's propeller, and the police searched his pockets in vain for means of identification. They contained nothing, however, save for a small note-book filled with jottings on the brooding period of the *Fringilla Canaria*.

'It is the wise man who keeps bees,' remarked Sherlock Holmes when he read the report. 'You know where you are with them and at least they do not attempt to represent themselves as something that they are not.'

> In this memorable year '95, a curious and incongruous succession of cases had engaged his attention ranging from . . . the sudden death of Cardinal Tosca down to the arrest of Wilson, the notorious canary-trainer,[1] which removed a plague-spot from the East End of London.
>
> FROM 'BLACK PETER'

[1] In the Wilson case, Holmes did not actually arrest Wilson, as Wilson was drowned. This was a typical Watson error in his hurried reference to the case in 'Black Peter'.

13

JOHN DICKSON CARR

'ANOTHER GLASS, WATSON!'

'He laid an envelope on the table, and we all bent over it.
It was of common quality, greyish in colour. The address,
"Sir Henry Baskerville, Northumberland Hotel", was
printed in rough characters . . .'

So writes Dr Watson in the fourth chapter of *The Hound of the
Baskervilles*. The game is afoot. A great case is in full cry. Mr
Sherlock Holmes and his colleague, not for the first time, are
about to meet some very rough characters indeed.

The Northumberland Hotel, presumably, was in Northumberland Avenue, and leading off the Avenue in Northumberland Street you will today find an inn named after the great
detective.

And it is right that we should find it there, for it was also in a
Northumberland Avenue hotel that Holmes traced Francis
Hay Moulton, the energetic American who had spirited away
Lord St Simon's bride in *The Noble Bachelor*. Northumberland
Avenue is close to Scotland Yard. It is also a stone's throw from
Charing Cross Station; Holmes and Watson, off for one of their
sudden dashes into the country, could always find a train leaving just when they wanted it. Nobody else has ever been able to
accomplish this.

From *The Illustrious Client* we learn that both the detective and
the doctor 'had a weakness for the Turkish bath'. They liked to
relax in the drying-room on the upper floor of the Northumberland Avenue establishment. The baths came to an end a few
years ago. But the building still remains, with its front door immediately outside the inn. Northumberland Avenue, heavy and
lowering, is in fact as full of romance as Baker Street itself.

It is even more fitting that an inn, a tavern, a pub, a chop-house (call it what you will) should be named after the most famous character in English fiction. An enthusiast for Mr Sherlock Holmes once suggested that there ought to be a statue to his memory. But this is all wrong. Statues are frozen, lifeless, exalted on their pedestals. There is nothing frozen about Sherlock Holmes. Even when he sits back in his chair, his eyes closed and his finger-tips together, he is as vibrant with life as when he crawls about a room in search of clues. A moment more, and he will leap from his chair; a moment more, and he will shed dressing-gown for frock-coat and top-hat, or the cloth cap which means war. In these matters the British have a sound, practical, romantic instinct. Statues are erected to those whom they admire or esteem. But inn-signs are reserved for those whom they both honour and love.

'The Sherlock Holmes'! Think, I beg of you, of that name and what it means.

It is as dreamlike as 'The Treasure Island', yet as homely as 'The Bull and Bush'. It does not suggest blood and corpses, however much such things may lurk in the background. On the contrary, it suggests the snug sitting-room upstairs: the cigars in the coal-scuttle, the fire and gaslight aglow: in short, the height of comfort and cosiness.

For Sherlock Holmes, despite his surface austerity, was the soul of hospitality. Few detectives can ever have been so be-devilled by their clients. They rout him out before dawn, as Helen Stoner did in *The Speckled Band*. They arrive with the hop, skip, and jump of near-madness, after the fashion of Alexander Holder, the banker in *The Beryl Coronet*. They burst into the room and faint on the hearthrug (Dr Thorneycroft Huxtable in *The Priory School*). Or, like the ungrateful Inspector Lestrade, they creep in to scoff at his methods and pick his brains.

It does not matter. Unruffled, unfailing, Sherlock Holmes gives them whisky or brandy if they are men (brandy is Watson's prescription for almost anything), and hot coffee if they are women. His ear is always attentive. Food can be, and is, provided in abundance.

'Mrs Hudson has risen to the occasion,' said Holmes, un-covering a dish of curried chicken. 'Her cuisine is a little limited, but she has as good an idea of breakfast as a Scotchwoman.'

This cryptic statement is significant; the conservative Watson ate ham and eggs. But it was a special occasion. At the breakfast-table, under cover of a dish, Holmes returns the stolen Naval Treaty to that unfortunate Foreign Office official who for weeks has lived under suspicion of having stolen it. Holmes' sense of the dramatic, perhaps, is a little ill-timed. The luckless Percy Phelps is so overcome with relief that he dances, shrieks, and collapses. Once more they are compelled to revive a client with brandy.

On the other hand, in the story of *The Noble Bachelor*, to which reference has been made, Holmes' sheer kindness of heart sets out a feast for his guests. 'A quite epicurean little cold supper,' declares Watson, 'began to be laid out upon our humble lodging-house mahogany. There were a couple of brace of cold woodcock, a pheasant, a *pâté-de-foie-gras* pie, with a group of ancient and cobwebby bottles.'

No nonsense, here, about Vitamin C or a balanced diet. Sherlock Holmes rubs his hands with pleasure at the sight. His delight, Watson indicates, comes less from the sight of the supper-table than from the prospect of uniting in friendship an affronted English bridegroom and a wayward American bride. But careful consideration must show us that far too much has been made of Holmes' indifference to the pleasures of the table.

Holmes never scorned food and drink. There were times when he simply forgot them. Absorbed in a complex case, as in the affair of John Openshaw and *The Five Orange Pips*, he returns shaken to Baker Street at 10 p.m. He looks pale and worn. Tearing a piece from a loaf of bread, he devours it voraciously with the cry that he is starving.

And yet he has had breakfast that morning; and both Holmes and Watson were tremendous breakfast-eaters at a late hour. Most of us, at a pinch, could go foodless for twelve hours without actually reeling. Holmes could do it, but it upset him.

The truth of his tastes may be seen with great clearness in *The Dying Detective*. Anguished, ghastly, he has gone for three days without food or drink to trap the murderer of poor Victor Savage. Belladonna and crusts of beeswax were hardly necessary as a disguise. That wild talk of oysters and half-crowns was

not all pretended delirium. Then the gaslight brightens; Mr
Culverton Smith snarls in the grip of the law. After dragging
deeply at a cigarette, Holmes' first call is for biscuits and a glass
of claret from his inexhaustible sideboard. But Mrs Hudson's
cuisine will no longer suffice; instead he carries away Watson
for a dinner at Simpson's.

Holmes' maternal ancestors were French. He loved his food,
and he needed it. Indeed, it would be possible to argue that the
aroma of good cooking and the bouquet of good wine rise as
pervasively through the stories as the tang of yellow fog or the
reek of shag tobacco. Good novels, they say, are full of inns.
Certainly good stories are full of plates and glasses; it is a part
of the Victorian scene, entwined in curtained cosiness, and the
adventures of Sherlock Holmes would be bleak without it.

He is very fond of dining in Italian restaurants: not only at
such well-known places as Frascati's in Oxford Street, but at
others which are more difficult to trace. There is Mancini's,
mentioned in *The Hound of the Baskervilles*. There is still another,
described as 'garish', to which Watson is abruptly summoned
during the quest for the Bruce-Partington plans.

'Am dining,' writes Holmes, 'at Goldini's Restaurant,
Gloucester Road, Kensington. Please come at once and join
me there. Bring with you a jemmy, a dark lantern, a chisel,
and a revolver.'

Watson has qualms, as well he may. The last time they
burgled somebody's house, he may have recalled, they were
obliged to leap on top of a six-foot wall, and then run two miles,
much of it across the switchback surface of Hampstead Heath in
the dark.

'Have you had something to eat?' rather casually demands
Sherlock Holmes, solicitous of everyone's comfort except
Watson's, when his companion arrives laden with burglar's
tools at Goldini's. 'Then join me in a coffee and curaçao.'

That occurred in the year '95, an *annus mirabilis*; Holmes has
not hitherto shown much interest in liqueurs. On the other hand,
his taste in drinks is as broad and catholic as Watson's own. In
addition to the famous tantalus, for ever flowing with spirits,
Holmes has put in a good store of claret and Burgundy. Of the
Burgundy we can be certain: a bottle of Beaune with lunch

gives Watson courage to protest about Holmes' use of cocaine. And he is cured of that habit to indulge a taste for better things. Assuredly his close attention to wine-bottles and cork-screws enables him to solve the problem of *The Abbey Grange* in '97.

But these are later cases. At the very beginning, in '81, a depressed Watson haunts the Criterion Bar. If he hadn't, he would not have encountered young Stamford and he would never have met Sherlock Holmes. The thought is too appalling to pursue. We need not accuse Watson of over-conviviality, as did the late Monsignor Knox, or say he was extravagant on his half-pay. As late as the year '91, according to Holmes, you could lunch at the very best hotel for half a crown. You could occupy its finest rooms (rooms, distinctly plural) for ten bob a night. And, if eightpence was a very steep price to pay for a glass of sherry, then a whole shilling for a cocktail must have seemed really intolerable.

Nostalgia, nostalgia, nostalgia!

During a joyous Christmas interlude, not long after the good doctor's marriage, we find Holmes and Watson drinking beer at the Alpha Inn, Bloomsbury. The affair of *The Blue Carbuncle* ends, as it should, at the supper-table. Even in the last chronological adventure—on the terrible August 2, 1914—their habits are unchanged.

Von Bork, the master-spy, has been foiled and outwitted. There is an east wind coming. 'Another glass, Watson!' exclaims a familiar voice from a gaunt man of sixty. On the edge of a world in ruins, above the last twinkling lights, they drink Imperial Tokay from the cellars of Franz Joseph at the Schoenbrunn Palace.

Last adventure? Gaunt man of sixty? No: this won't do. Holmes is immortal, like D'Artagnan or Sam Weller; he does not age or grow infirm; he is still with us. Such a reflection alone must gladden the heart of any wayfarer in London who sees on the new hanging sign in Northumberland Street the familiar profile.

Above all it must gladden the heart of Mr Holmes himself. 'By Jove, Watson!' We can fancy the lean figure stiffening in the mist, the imperious gesture to Watson, the door eagerly pushed open. Now Sherlock Holmes, it is true, would never consent to visit openly a place named in his honour. Essentially a modest man, despite all his quirks of vanity, he would revolt through all his fastidious soul. But it would delight him to prowl there in disguise.

In the old days, we know, the perfection of his disguises was equalled only by their staggering variety. They ranged from a Tibetan Lama to a French *ouvrier*; from Sigerson, the Norwegian explorer, to Captain Basil, the swaggering sea-dog. As a clergy-man he deceived Irene Adler. As an old bookseller he made Watson faint. As a plumber named Escott he wooed and won the housemaid of Charles Augustus Milverton. Imagination boggles at what disguise he would assume in 'The Sherlock Holmes'.

Yet how those deep-set eyes would glisten, those long and nervous fingers twitch, to revisit the scene of his glory among the criminal relics he loved! Climbing a staircase that might be that of 221B Baker Street, he would find his own room little changed, his possessions and his effects just as he left them—the dressing-gown on its hook, tobacco in the Persian slipper, unanswered letters still affixed to the mantelpiece and his decoy bust still in the window to mislead Colonel Sebastian Moran. Downstairs in the bars are the relics of his famous cases. In *his* day the relics were not so neat or tidy. In *his* day they had a way of wandering into unlikely positions, and turning up in the butter-dish. But they are nearly all here, from the great hound affrighting the air to John Straker's cataract-knife and the King of Bohemia's snuff-box.

And so, should you yourself be there one quiet night, be sure to look carefully if covertly about you. That stolid businessman by the bar-counter, that Foreign Office official at the restaurant-table, may not be quite what they seem. As a train whistles from Charing Cross you may catch a flash from the keen eyes of Sherlock Holmes—or think you hear the great-hearted chuckle of Sir Arthur Conan Doyle.

14

JAMES EDWARD HOLROYD

'OUR CLIENT'S FOOT UPON THE STAIR'

Not the least familiar and fascinating aspect of the Baker Street saga is the almost incredible procession of visitors. Ladies and gentlemen in various urgencies of distress, harassed callers from The Yard, occasional bold crooks fearlessly bearding the clean-shaven lion in his den—all sooner or later made the journey up the seventeen stairs to the cosy sitting-room at 221 B. Frequently the visitations are at inconvenient hours—before dawn, in time to interrupt breakfast, or when Holmes and Watson are settling down for a quiet evening before the fire.

Indeed from the most casual re-reading of the adventures, it is clear that the partners seldom achieve the luxury of a night off duty. The wilder the weather without, the more is the peace of what Watson called 'our snug sanctum' likely to be dis-turbed.

In their rare moments of repose one fancies that Watson is the more restless partner. Not only had he fewer hobby horses to ride, but as the man of action—at least before his marriages—he scarcely suggests the pattern of domesticity. While Holmes would be totally absorbed in one of his many scholarly interests —Lassus, a medieval palimpsest or the latest monograph— Watson, one leg thrown stiffly across the other, would doubtless stare moodily into the fire or stealthily turn a page of the yellow-back he was reading under cover of some medical treatise.

It is Holmes who declares that his mind rebels against stag-nation, but I believe that Watson is the one who is more irked by inactivity. Holmes, as we know, could be at once the most silent and the most exasperating of stable-companions, and I fancy that Watson's thoughts must often have drifted to the

Criterion bar or to the billiards-room of his club as he perforce settled in to one of those timeless evenings at 221 B. Indeed, it seems to be an indication of his restlessness that we sometimes find him peering out of their first-floor window. Perhaps the old wound was troublesome on these occasions and he sought distraction; or perhaps Holmes was toying with his malodorous chemicals or reaching for the violin. Whatever the reason, we are pretty certain to hear the clatter of hooves at the kerb, the pealing door-bell and Holmes' omniscient (and in truth somewhat infuriating): 'Here, if I mistake not, is our client's foot upon the stair.'

I believe that Watson welcomed visitors not only because they promised some new excitement and the chance of adding a new chapter to his reminiscences (did he ever offer Holmes a share of the royalties?), but because they enabled him to step into the picture and to dilute the oppressive atmosphere of Holmes solus. To most of us, the ringing of the bell at all hours would have been as great a nuisance as the telephone. But not, I think, to Watson.

Off-hand I can recall only two evenings when the Baker Street scene was not interrupted by a visitor. They occur in *The Gloria Scott* and *The Musgrave Ritual*, consecutive adventures of Holmes' early career before he went into partnership. Whenever I re-read these two adventures I find myself listening behind the narrative—as Watson himself perhaps listened—for the ring of the street door-bell. It is not to diminish the doctor's undoubted admiration for his friend to suggest that he may sometimes have become slightly bored by the great man's long monologues. Watson of course put a loyal face on things: recorded, for instance, a merry meal in which Holmes spoke in quick succession 'on miracle plays, on medieval pottery, on Stradivarius violins, and on the warships of the future'. Merry may not have been the exact word, but it is clear that Watson's role was simply that of a large and patient ear. Doubtless he would have preferred to get in a word or two about his Afghan experiences; but what chance had he against a genius who handled every subject 'as though he had made a special study of it'? That the good Watson sometimes found that visitors appreciated his old campaigning stories—one recalls how Miss Mary Morstan was impressed—might be regarded as an additional reason why he would welcome the ring of the door-bell.

As for Holmes, one feels that he must indeed have played the game for the game's own sake to have greeted his callers with such uniform urbanity at such unexpected hours. One is warmed by the slightly old-world manner with which he sets each at ease: a glass of whisky for the inspector, a seat by the fire for the dripping visitant with the clay and chalk of the south-west still clinging to his toecaps. Holmes may occasionally have forced the pace in his anxiety to elucidate all the facts. One does not readily forget his lapse when sweet Mary Morstan choked back a sob as she spoke of her father's disappearance: ' "The date?" asked Holmes opening his note-book.'

It could not always have been easy for Holmes to tear him-self away from some complicated piece of research in order to plunge into an adventure which might end in the nearly trivial. And even if Watson really welcomed visitors, it does not follow that he felt equal enthusiasm for the awkward excursions which so frequently became their corollary. Many of the calls were in fact of a kind to test the toughest fibre. To Aldgate in dense fog; to Croydon with the thermometer at 90 degrees; supper-less to the 'Alpha' Inn on a night so bitter that 'the breaths of the passers-by blew out into smoke like so many pistol-shots'. Their inhospitable journeyings suggest dedication of a high order.

Most of the impressive, and indeed some of the unimpressive, visitors to Baker Street are memorably netted in the long series of illustrations which accompanied the adventures down the years in the pages of the old *Strand* magazine. For most English readers the supreme artist was Sidney Paget, the centenary of whose birth occurred in 1960. But before turning to the well-loved pages of the early *Strand*, one must glance at *A Study in Scarlet*, the novel in which Holmes first appeared and in which we may fancy that both author and illustrators were feeling for a method. It is a minor point of history that in this first story it did not occur to D. H. Friston to depict 221B in any of the five drawings made for its original appearance in Beeton's *Christmas Annual* of 1887. Nor were George Hutchinson's forty illustrations for the third edition of 1891 more rewarding. Four only of the set give any glimpse of the 221B interior, and even then it is any indeterminate sitting-room anywhere. I think his drawings even provide some kind of support for Michael Harrison's amiable heretical theory that this Baker Street was not in W1 but in Clerkenwell or Brixton.

Suddenly, however, and in this same year of 1891, the saga became authentic, put on immortality. With a stroke of genius Conan Doyle invented the brief self-contained episode which introduced Holmes and Watson to a new and growing audience in the youthful *Strand*. The immediate importance to the author was that he had hit on a device whose obvious advantages over the traditional serial clearly made it more acceptable to editors of periodicals. But in a larger sense, the significance of the short-story form into which the adventures were now mainly cast was that the detective and his chronicler became the centre of action instead of merely serving as the sparse covering for slabs of alien villainry played out in India or the Far West.

In the early *Strand* Holmes in fact became indubitably Holmes of Baker Street and from 1891 to 1927 the pages of the magazine intermittently echoed the sound of the client's foot upon the stair. We must always count it as the greatest of good fortune that Sidney Paget, a London artist who had already exhibited in the Royal Academy, was at hand to set the scene for 221 B. Yet how casually the fates move. There is a tradition in the Paget family that Greenough Smith, the editor of the *Strand* wanted Sidney's brother Walter as illustrator but confused their identity. Walter Paget was a considerable artist in his own right, but when one recalls his somewhat stilted drawings for *The Dying Detective* after his brother's death, one is glad that the original commission went to Sidney. Walter none the less achieved an oblique immortality, for his brother used him as a model for Holmes and so the great investigator's features became more personable than Conan Doyle's original conception of 'a thin, razor-like face with a great hawk's-bill of a nose and two small eyes set close together on either side of it'.

The face that solved a thousand crimes is certainly more debonair than this as Holmes, standing back to fire, looks down at Watson at the beginning of *A Scandal in Bohemia*. Since there are three or four pages of print between us and the slow and heavy step which announces the arrival of the first illustrious client, let us pause nostalgically to savour the scene.

It is Sidney Paget's first drawing for the saga and it carries for us the same ineluctable sense of rightness and authority as for those privileged seniors who were able to turn the exciting blue-green covers of the magazine over seventy years ago.

The actual date of the adventure is March 20, 1888, which would make Holmes thirty-four and Watson a year or two older. Do they appear more mature than this in Paget's first drawing? Perhaps they are nearer to those middle forties in which one tends to fix them in memory; perhaps because the clothes of the period added to age. Holmes, for example, is wearing a smart frock-coat, his hands comfortably hidden in its folds as befits a man standing on his own hearth. Watson, seated in one of the familiar and castored arm-chairs with a carved wooden frame-work, has a hint of velvet collar. He wears the choker and stock proper to a doctor who has just visited a patient. Holmes, however, affects the somewhat less formal black bow tucked under the edges of his collar in the style now popular with the younger black-tie brigade. I do not know of any canonical authority for Holmes' neckwear and it seems likely that Paget—who was later to invent the equally characteristic deerstalker—possibly adapted this A. J. Balfour style from Hutchinson's drawings.

In this first illustration by Paget one is strongly aware of his feeling for the atmosphere of 221 B. The whole scene is aglow with firelight. There are massive fire-irons in the fender (one recalls that Watson was apt to reach for the poker in moments of crisis), two lamps, a clock and a vase on the mantelshelf. In the shadows we see a tall bureau-bookcase and at Watson's foot the coal-scuttle in which Holmes unaccountably kept his cigars. To complete the comfortable picture Watson is smoking —not, however, a coal-scuttle vintage, for he tells us that on this occasion Holmes 'threw across his case of cigars, and indicated a spirit case and a gasogene in the corner'.

So the curtain rises and after a glancing and tantalizing allusion to recent investigations—the Trepoff murder at Odessa and the singular tragedy of the Atkinson brothers at Trincomalee—and some characteristic deductive work by the Master, we hear what with tingling expectancy we have been waiting to hear: 'the sharp sound of horses' hooves and grating wheels against the kerb'.

For sheer barbaric magnificence there could not have been a more dramatic curtain-raiser either for the series or for Paget's prentice hand. The Herculean stature of the visitant, the cloak of deep blue and flame, the astrakhan slashings, the fur-trimmed jack-boots, the mysterious black mask. Finally, the sonorous title, reverberating like a roll of Wagnerian drums: 'Wilhelm Gottsreich Sigismond von Ormstein, Grand Duke of Cassel-Felstein, and hereditary King of Bohemia.' One wonders what Mrs Hudson thought of this apparition when she answered the door.[1] Watson, if one is to judge from his prose which suddenly flames like the enormous single beryl at the throat of majesty, was clearly impressed, but recovered sufficiently to note that so rich a costume 'would, in England, be looked upon as akin to bad taste'. Holmes alone remained cool; he even yawned at one stage of the interview. Perhaps as a result of his delicate services for so many of the leading royal families he really regarded this Middle-European princeling as somewhat small beer. Or maybe the manner stemmed from his flair for deflating pomposity. Either way the front was impeccably kept. Even when the king finally flung down the heavy chamois bag containing three hundred pounds in gold and seven hundred in notes for expenses, Holmes calmly scribbled a receipt on a sheet of his note-book.

From the artist's point of view it must have seemed a long step down from this majestic opening to the slow-witted red-headed pawnbroker in the next adventure and the even more stupid Mary Sutherland (who failed to recognize her own step-father and arrived at 221 B wearing odd shoes) in the third. I suppose that one of the trials of an illustrator is that he must not have favourites; he is required to delineate the indifferent as well as the different. Members of the Sherlock Holmes Society of London, assembling for their annual variations of the gas-fitters' ball, naturally tend to appear as Dr Grimesby Roylott, '*the* woman' and similar strongly individualized characters; but Paget had also to give a semblance of reality to a multitude of Angel Hosmers, Victor Hatherleys and bewildered bankers before reaching his moments of exaltation. One would

[1] When this appeared in the *Cornhill*, Sir Sydney Roberts blandly reminded me that *A Scandal in Bohemia* was in fact the one adventure in which Holmes referred to the landlady as 'Mrs Turner'.

like to feel that in sketching these minor figures he was working up to the superb climax of Moriarty.

In these early drawings Paget appears to have solved the problem of the incidental scenes by concentrating on a few essentials. Thus the only article of furniture shown in the interview with Alexander Holder, the banker, is the chair in which he sits and even this appears to be a sawn-off version. Similarly, for the fireside lecture given by Holmes in *The Copper Beeches* the two familiar arm-chairs have to serve as sole properties save for the additional master touch of the tongs which hold the glowing coal for Holmes' pipe. At this stage the contents of the sitting room have in fact to be synthesized from individual drawings—the sofa and small wooden chair from *The Blue Carbuncle*, the cane chair from *The Greek Interpreter*, the complete dining-table (with Watson, not Holmes, at its head) in the breakfast denouement of *The Naval Treaty*.

'Is there any other point which I can make clear?' Holmes asks in the last-named adventure and immediately a flood of queries rises in the mind. Just where was the safe for the black pearl of the Borgias; the portraits, framed and unframed, of General Gordon and Henry Ward Beecher, the wall with the patriotic VRS pocked in bullet-holes, the table for the chemicals?

The answers to some of these queries may emerge in later illustrations. But new problems also. After the ominous appearance of Professor Moriarty (his face 'slowly oscillating from side to side in a curiously reptilian fashion') in the *Strand* magazine in 1893, nearly eight years were to pass before Dr James Mortimer, the man of science, became the next visitor to climb the stairs to consult Holmes in the overture to the classic *Hound*. I think that Dr Mortimer was a very odd character indeed. To begin with, Watson's description of him ('a very tall thin man, with a long nose like a beak, which jutted out between two keen grey eyes, set closely together') is almost an exact transcript of Conan Doyle's original conception of Holmes. Then the mystery—not satisfactorily explained by Holmes' guess at lack of ambition—of why a man with a distinguished medical career should bury himself in the heart of Dartmoor. Next, those slightly bizarre interests—'charming evenings' discussing the comparative anatomy of the Bushman and the Hottentot with Sir Charles Baskerville; 'pure amusement' visiting the museum of the Royal College of Surgeons. All in all a somewhat sinister figure; but one to whom we are nevertheless eternally grateful for that dramatic chapter-ending whose sibilance comes whispering down the years: 'Mr Holmes, they were the footprints of a gigantic hound.'

Sidney Paget certainly spread his talent on Dr Mortimer in eleven drawings. It is good to see that even the austere man of science permitted himself a measure of relaxation, for while in ten of them he wears the silk hat and frock-coat appropriate to the professional man visiting London, in the eleventh, at Baskerville Hall, he has become a trim figure in double-breasted jacket and straw boater.

But if we are to turn a pocket-lens on to background as well as foreground, it is the first illustration to the *Hound* which halts our interest. As Dr Mortimer crosses the threshold of the sitting-room at 221 B, we note that some extraordinary changes have occurred during the intervening years. The door now opens inwards, hinged left; when we last saw it—at the close of *A Case of Identity*—it opened outwards, hinged right. I take it to be the same door since there is a tall bureau-bookcase (a twin to the one near the fireplace?) shown to its left in both illustrations. Moreover, while a window in *The Case of Identity* drawing is shown on the right-hand wall, in that of the *Hound* the window is on the opposite wall. I accept Sidney Paget's view on the latter point because it accords with my theory that there must have been a rear window to give credibility to Watson's statement in *The Cardboard Box* that the morning sun was reflected on the walls of houses opposite 221 B. As it is generally agreed that Mrs Hudson's domain was on the west side of the street, the houses opposite face west and could not have reflected the glare of morning sunshine. But houses at the back of 221 B would face east and Watson could have been looking at them through a rear window just before falling into his memorable brown study. Paget thus accidentally confirms my tentative solution of one of the most baffling problems in the saga.

But these are deep waters, Watson. Sufficient to note that after the long leap forward to Dartmoor, the only remaining glimpse of 221 B comes with the two illustrations in the final chapter of the *Hound* when the partners have returned and Holmes, comfortably relaxed with dressing-gown and pipe, gives his customary succinct recapitulation. It is a raw foggy evening at the end of November and the fire blazes invitingly. I am weak enough to admit that not even the promise of a little dinner at Marcini's followed by the De Reszkes in *Les Huguenots* would have persuaded me to go out on such a night. The arrival of a client just then would have seemed to me a Devil's Foot upon the stair. The lights were out and I fear I should have quietly bolted the door and pretended I was not at home!

With the *Return* series, which opened in the *Strand* in 1903, we arrive reluctantly at the close of Sidney Paget's long association. One's regret is the keener because the artist as well as the principal character had put on stature over the years. Some of the drawings in the new series, such as the capture of Abe Slaney and the tussle between Holmes and old Colonel Moran, have a powerful maturity which in turn was substantially enhanced by improved technical reproduction.

The thirteen adventures bring an exceptional sequence of visitors up the narrow stairs. In many ways the most remarkable of all must have been the return of the Master himself— an appearance that threw Mrs Hudson into violent hysterics as it later caused even the phlegmatic Watson to faint. How one wishes in passing that Paget had preserved for us the scene in which the faithful landlady crept into the sitting-room on all fours to change the position of the wax bust. It is a moment to which devotion would have given its own dignity.

But after Holmes himself, what a pilgrimage of personalities: Violet Smith, the solitary cyclist, 'young and beautiful . . . tall, graceful and queenly' and incidentally one of a cluster of four violets in the saga; Lestrade, bull-doggy as ever; the hirsute and powerful harpooner; that smooth operator Charles Augustus Milverton, well deserving his title of 'the worst man in London'; and, as climax to the whole series, the Prime Minister and his Secretary for European Affairs—a title that becomes increasingly prophetic, though the description of the owner as being 'endowed with every beauty of body and of mind' is a Watsonism that would make any politician wince.

As they come and go we gain new intelligence about 221B. A small Indian coffee table makes its appearance at the close of

The Empty House, an inlaid side-table with candlestick in *Milverton*, an adjustable metal table-lamp in *The Six Napoleons*, a different kind of lamp with a flouncy feminine shade in *The Golden Pince-nez*, and so on.

Two drawings on consecutive pages of *The Norwood Builder* are especially rewarding. They show, respectively, the arrival and departure (under arrest) of 'the unhappy John Hector McFarlane'. The closest attention has been given to the duplication of the contents of the breakfast table and to the subsequent changes in the disposition of chairs. In the first illustration, for example, Holmes is seated at the table with a newspaper on his lap. In the second, he has taken up the familiar arm-chair pose, legs stretched and finger-tips together. The newspaper has fallen to the floor and the dining-chair he has vacated stands empty at the table. There are similar touches of exact observation. But, alas! the door has again been playing tricks. Not only does it now open inwards, *hinged right*, but the four short and two double-length panels in the first drawing have become three pairs of identical size in the second! By the time we reach the entry of Captain Croker in *The Abbey Grange* it has changed again to a left-side hinge but still opening inwards; while the tall bookcase-bureau, hitherto either on the left of the fireplace or to the left of the door, is now on the right-hand side of the fireplace.

In Sidney Paget's behalf I would contend that the furniture was probably moved around from time to time. As for the unpredictable door, is it not possible that some system of hidden draughts whistled up the seventeen stairs and that the tetchy Holmes had the local carpenter experiment with different positions to see if it could be overcome?

The way of the illustrator is hard and if I make a further point about Sidney Paget's drawings it will be only in the affectionate mood of warts-and-all. It is that in this final series he fell into the fallacy of depicting Holmes and Watson as noticeably older than in the earlier drawings. Throughout the *Return* Holmes' hair has begun to recede and Watson's moustache and figure have perhaps lost something of their first bloom. This is because thirteen years elapsed between the first illustrations and the last.

As it happens, an exact comparison is possible. Paget's first illustrations for the first short story, *A Scandal in Bohemia*, to which I have already referred, is paralleled by a similar scene in *The Second Stain*, the final story of the *Return* series. The first appeared in the *Strand* of July 1891, the other in the *Strand* of December 1904. By the happiest of full circles the later drawing faithfully echoes the earlier one. Holmes again stands before the fire, Watson once more lounges in an arm-chair to the left of it. The chair is slightly different; it has doubtless replaced the earlier one. Clock and lamp are still on the mantelshelf, but again of different pattern. On Watson's left the bookcase-bureau survives unchanged. But although the most casual glance suggests that the partners have aged in the second drawing, the chronological evidence is that the adventure of the second stain occurred in the same year as that of the scandal in Bohemia, if not indeed somewhat earlier.

Does the calendar then fault the artist? Not, I think, in any significant sense. What we have to remember is that the date of *The Empty House*—the opening adventure of the *Return* series—was undoubtedly 1894. It marked what was Holmes' second career. He had defeated Moriarty and had only returned to London after three years of wandering round the world from Tibet to southern France. He was clearly a more seasoned character than he had been in the earlier *Strand* appearances whatever the dates assigned by the text. And it was this first adventure of the *Return* that justifiably fixed the image for the drawings for the twelve subsequent adventures.

I believe that one could have enlisted support for Sidney Paget's view from the late Bernard Darwin, that doyen of Sherlockians, who held the Fundamentalist creed that ignored internal dating and regarded the first published story as the first, the second as the second and so on. By the light of this sturdy, if over-simple faith Sidney Paget could have maintained that by the time the *Return* stories appeared in print in 1903–4 Holmes had already retired and was only two or three adventures away from the great climacteric of *His Last Bow* in 1914. In holding this view the artist may indeed have found an instinctive way to the larger truth, content to leave the petty squabblings about dates to the pettifogging commentator of today! Either way we salute his memory as the artist who not only gave us a Holmes and Watson who are perfectly in period but who also took us authentically behind the scenes at 221B.

Paget died in 1908 and a separate chapter could be written about the succession of excellent artists—Arthur Twidle, Frank Wiles, H. M. Brock, Howard Elcock, Alfred Gilbert and others—who continued to illustrate the remaining adventures in the *Strand*. In one sense, however, everything had been said; for the later illustrators substantially followed the prototypes that Paget had created. In some respects they had a freer hand with drawings which sometimes spread over two pages. But I do not think that Holmes and Watson come closer because writ larger. Indeed, with the closing of Sidney Paget's reign I feel something of the same diminution of interest as when the last of the old Forsytes disappeared from Galsworthy's saga.

One of the Paget family treasures—a wedding gift to the artist—is a silver cigarette case inscribed 'from Sherlock Holmes 1893'. Since *Strand* readers had been led to believe that Holmes had perished with Moriarty in the Reichenbach fall two years earlier, and as subsequent history revealed that he had in fact visited many far-off places during the great absence of 1891–4, the receipt at that date of a gift bearing an English hall-mark might have been held to contain the elements of a problem that the detective himself would have appreciated. We may nevertheless safely conclude that the cigarette case was sent either by Sir Arthur Conan Doyle or by Dr Watson as an appropriate testimonial to Sidney Paget's share in shaping the most famous profile in the world.

⇒❋ 15 ❋⇐

W. S. BRISTOWE

THE TRUTH ABOUT MORIARTY

After searching my conscience I have decided that I cannot suppress a document of great importance which has come into my hands, despite the pain and anxiety it has caused me and may cause others. This document gives the Moriarty family's version of what happened on May 4, 1891, at the Reichenbach Falls, together with an account of the events leading up to that final encounter between Sherlock Holmes and Professor Moriarty, and the long drawn out aftermath.

The early part of the present document must resemble closely the contents of Colonel James Moriarty's letters, which Watson described in 1893 as an 'absolute perversion of the facts'. The Colonel's failure to publish them in Britain can probably be attributed to the influence of Mycroft Holmes. Remember in this connection that Sherlock Holmes once described his brother as being at times 'the Government' so his influence over the Press must have been immense and their fear of a libel action considerable.

I confess that the present document fills me with grave unease and I must leave others to make their own agonizing reappraisal of the events described by Watson in *The Final Problem* and *The Empty House* after studying these cases afresh with the utmost care. Watson's honesty and his loyalty to Holmes cannot be questioned, and in writing as he did we may detect some evidence of doubts in his mind which loyalty to his friend did not allow him to express. This is brought about in the Moriarty document. When calling his account *The Final Problem* it is possible that the honest Watson was admitting that the interpretation of events he had experienced still remained a problem to him.

144

One final thing—no address accompanies the long letter which follows, so I cannot put members of the Society in touch with Mr James Moriarty.

August 1960   W. S. Bristowe

LETTER FROM MR JAMES MORIARTY

Dear Dr Bristowe,

For reasons which must be obvious to all, I have never sought membership of the Sherlock Holmes Society. Nevertheless I have wondered if that Society would do me the courtesy of publishing this letter? It would do an old man good to vent some of his pent-up bitterness before he dies and I alone am able to give the answers to questions which still puzzle members of the Society.

I must start by explaining who I am. I am the son of Colonel James Moriarty of the Indian Army, and *not* of his brother, Professor James Moriarty, the brilliant scientist. Vile prejudice, of which I have experienced plenty, makes it necessary for me to say this although everybody knows that my uncle, Professor Moriarty, was never married.

I must also pour scorn on those ignorant people who have seized on my grandfather's choice of James as the name for two of his sons, in order to imply that this simple act is part of a pattern explaining 'hereditary tendencies of a most diabolical kind'. Your own genealogical studies, of which I happen to be aware, have revealed such a whim as being nothing more than an admirable old-English custom going back to the sixteenth century. Amongst your own kinsmen did not Richard Bristowe of Horley and his brother John of Leigh make clear in their Wills in 1530 and 1532 respectively that both had two sons living named John? And did not one of the four Johns mention his own two daughters Anne in his Will of 1588? This was no peculiarity of your family and mine, for here are two examples from Suffolk pedigrees:

1. John Snell of Cockfield, buried in 1568, mentioned in his Will *three* sons named John.

2. Thomas Harvey of Nayland provided for nine sons in his

Will in 1571 who included Robert the elder, Robert the younger, John the elder and John the younger.

Now, although I do not belong to your Society, I make a point of reading its *Journal* to see what monstrous charges are made against my uncle and his associates. It was therefore with mixed feelings of exultation and hope that I read Mr J. E. Holroyd's contribution. Here he says: 'I have never seen any satisfactory explanation of Watson's curious conduct both before and after Reichenbach. In the first place why did he conceal from the world for two years the true facts about the supposed death of his friend at the fatal Falls? He claimed that his hand had been forced by the revelations published by Moriarty's brother.'

Mr Holroyd then points to the extraordinary behaviour of Watson in keeping 'the world in the dark for something like nine years after Holmes' actual return'.

Why indeed? I can give him the answers to these questions and to all the others which have perplexed Watson's and Holmes' admirers.

Let me start by posing some additional questions, all of which I will then answer. Why did Holmes warn Professor Moriarty on a Friday that he and his gang would be arrested on the following Monday? Why did he reject Watson's advice to arrest him on such stupid grounds that the smaller 'fish' in the organization would escape if the big ones were arrested? Why did Holmes decide to flee to the Continent for safety at such a time when his 'career had reached its summit', and when we know that 'he had at least five small refuges in different parts of London in which he was able to change his personality'? Had he ever shown fear for his own safety? Or demonstrated faith enough in the police to leave them to arrest such a large and cunning organization as the entire Moriarty gang without his personal help? And why, having seen Moriarty making for a Channel port on the Saturday, and having deduced that he would proceed to Paris, did he make no attempt to stop him? And why did he expect him to return two days later in time to be arrested, and then, 'with a bitter curse', fling the police telegram in the grate on the Monday and groan, 'I might have known it. He has escaped!'

Surely the members of your Sherlock Holmes Society are not

such dim-bulbs as Watson? There is only one possible answer and that happens to be the true one—that *Holmes wanted Professor Moriarty to escape.* Why? Please let me tell you.

Although I was only a lad in 1891 I heard the full story from my father many times before he died in 1902. In repeating this story I shall make no attempt to whitewash my uncle. Some of the story is in agreement with Watson's account; the remainder is supported by common sense and not by the nonsense of the Watson version. Mind you, in defence of Watson, he never knew the truth although at times he must have had his suspicions.

I will start by explaining a few things about my uncle's life. Born about 1846, he had already written a brilliant treatise on the Binomial Theorem at the age of twenty-one which had had a European vogue. At an unusually early age he won the Mathematical Chair at a provincial university. In his *Dynamics of an Asteroid* it is believed that he glimpsed the epoch-making discoveries attributed later to Einstein.

At this period of his life he lived for scientific research and art. Both were expensive. He needed apparatus which his small university could not afford, whilst art to him meant the purchase of pictures by Greuze and other artists costing thousands of pounds. He could indulge in neither on his salary of £700 so his burning ambitions got the better of him and he devoted his amazing brain to crime. Dark stories eventually got into circulation which were sufficient without proof to lose him his university chair. Under cover of being an Army coach, he then came to London in the late 'eighties and built up a criminal organization in London so skilfully that the threads never led back from his agents to the hub where he did the planning.

It did not take long for his enterprises to attract the attention of Sherlock Holmes but the fact is that my uncle was far too clever for him. Such successes as Holmes had had in the field of detection depended on facts and on deductions based on logical behaviour. My uncle knew this, he had studied Holmes' methods and he provided him with plenty of facts, but these were cunningly designed to lead him away from the correct solution. Behaviour which was logical for lesser minds was not followed by the subtler actions of the Professor.

As his defeats multiplied, Holmes became more and more

exasperated. They were intolerable to a man of his immense vanity and conceit. His health suffered, as Watson was not slow to notice, and he must have been on the verge of another breakdown in April 1891 of the kind he had experienced three or four years earlier.

Even to Watson, Holmes admitted that Professor Moriarty had 'one of the first brains in Europe', that he was 'a genius' and that he was his own 'intellectual equal'. Please notice these quotations if you happened to criticize my use of the word 'vanity' in the last paragraph! Such a man was incapable of admitting that this Napoleon of crime was greater than he, though as time went by the realization of this must have become an obsession. To Watson he said that he must crown his career 'with the capture and extinction of the most dangerous and capable criminal in Europe'. What he meant was that his failure to remove Professor Moriarty from society by legal means had brought him to the point where he must take the law into his own hands and exterminate him.

Perhaps you doubt this? Very well. Start, I beg you, by re-reading the sixty published cases and remember there were hundreds of others which Sherlock Holmes never allowed Watson to record. Even in the cases which passed Holmes' censorship you will find that he constantly flouted and broke the law. In one of their earliest associations he said to Watson, 'You don't mind breaking the law?' Elsewhere he said, 'I had rather play tricks with the law of England than with my own conscience'. And 'I suppose I shall have to compound a felony as usual'. The cases are crammed with a wide variety of serious offences including illegal entries, burglaries, thefts, felonies, breach of promise, fraud, blackmail and being an accessory after the fact to a murder. This is not a complete catalogue but it will suffice to illustrate how constantly he took the law into his own hands. 'It is every man's business to see justice done' he said on one occasion, and what he meant is made clear in another case where he actually became the law himself and acted as judge after appointing Watson as jury. His vanity and his contempt for the law knew no bounds. He was the arbiter of justice and he had now decided it was necessary and right to exterminate Professor Moriarty. On more than one occasion Holmes had not arrested or handed over to the police murderers who had taken lives in what he considered to be just causes, so why should he be expected to hesitate about committing such a murder himself?

Holmes' motive—his dual motive—is made clear when Watson records him as saying: ' . . . if I could beat that man, if I could free society of him . . .' That had become his obsession—and note the order of the two sentences.

Holmes' contempt for the law and his readiness to take the law into his own hands is abundantly clear from the examples I have given above. The police were well aware of this too and we have Lestrade's warning: 'Some of these days you'll go too far.' To quote Holmes himself: 'Art in the blood is liable to take the strangest forms.'

I am giving you a lot of quotations, I fear, in order to show you that my father's analysis was not a fabrication of his own bias or imagination. Let me give you two more before I describe, stage by stage, Holmes' intricate plot. In Watson's words: 'He pushed to an extreme the axiom that the only safe plotter was he who plotted alone.' Put beside this Holmes' statement of his own philosophy: 'What you do in this world is a matter of no consequence. The question is, what can you make people believe you have done.' Nothing could be more apt in demonstrating his cynical lack of conscience in plotting a murder which he would convince others was not a murder.

In the spring of 1891 Sherlock Holmes found himself in a position to arrest the entire gang except for the Professor himself whom again he had failed fully to implicate. This was the moment he selected to take the law into his own hands.

The first stage of his carefully laid plan started with three interviews on the same day, interviews with Scotland Yard, with Professor Moriarty and with Watson, in that order.

It was a Friday in April when he handed over to Scotland Yard all the evidence he had collected to enable them to arrest the ill-famed Moriarty gang. Instead of asking them to make the arrests at once he insisted that they should wait until the Monday, by which time, he assured them, he would have acquired the additional evidence necessary to include Professor Moriarty himself in the net.

Meanwhile he had, it seems, sent a carefully worded message to my uncle inviting him to Baker Street, guaranteeing his safety and hinting that in discussion lay his only chance of salvation. They met and Holmes disclosed how close he was on the track of his gang and implied that the entire gang, including the Professor himself, would be arrested on the following Monday. Having delivered this warning of coming events my father's understanding was that Holmes invited my uncle to make a complete confession of all his crimes which of course he scornfully declined to do. Then they parted.

Holmes' next action was to do some play-acting with Watson. This he had always enjoyed doing but now it was of vital importance for Watson was to be an important witness in case of need. From Watson's faithful account of Holmes' visit we see that Holmes spoke of threats by my uncle, followed by three attempts on his life. He stimulated intense fear and begged Watson to flee with him to the Continent to escape more murderous attacks by the Moriarty gang before they were arrested on the following Monday.

Watson was greatly moved and agreed to join him on the next express train in the morning. In order to impress Watson still further, Holmes gave him an intricate route to follow on his way to Victoria in order to avoid being followed.[1]

Notice at this point how Holmes, who had simulated intense fear so effectively, strode out into the night alone though twice invited to accept a bed in Watson's house. He gave as his reason that he would be 'a dangerous guest' and then did his utmost to avoid being seen leaving the house by climbing over the garden wall. If he was observed he would be in great danger himself; if he was not observed Watson would be in danger from watchers who thought his dangerous guest was still in the house. Do those admirers who have accepted his story find his intense fear and his flight to the Continent in keeping with his character? And would he really have exposed Watson to the danger in which he left him if his story were true?

[1] Holmes had started to build up the sinister nature of Professor Moriarty in *The Valley of Fear* case and had found Scotland Yard somewhat sceptical, so he was going to take no chance with Watson. 'We think in the CID that you have a wee bit of a bee in your bonnet over this Professor' was Inspector MacDonald's comment. This case was published twenty-one years later than *The Final Problem* although the events took place about two years earlier, so some confusion has arisen through Watson saying he had heard of Professor Moriarty in the earlier and that he had never heard of him in the later case. By 1914 when *The Valley of Fear* was published it would have seemed too ridiculous to Watson to say he had never heard of him!

The fact is that he still had work to do. There was the mysterious fire to be started at 221B Baker Street in such a way as to do no serious damage before the nearest fire engines came galloping along Baker Street to put it out. This was to be interpreted as yet another threat or attempt on his life by Professor Moriarty.

Holmes' tasks for the Friday night had now been completed. The police would make arrests on the Monday. Watson was convinced of the extreme danger from Professor Moriarty. And Moriarty—what would he do?

Holmes must have tried to place himself in the Professor's position and decided that he would start by trying to make contact with his leading London agents. Telephones were not, of course, in general use at that date so he would approach some of their homes with extreme caution and then withdraw in order to avoid being implicated when he saw police observers clumsily concealing themselves in doorways. Still more cautiously he would reconnoitre the approaches to his own home, find them unguarded, enter, pack and move as quickly as possibly to some obscure hotel under an assumed name. He would then catch the first train in the morning from Victoria for the Continent. Holmes had worked all this out before visiting Watson and this is why he had already reserved a compartment.

Why would the Professor catch the Continental Express and where would he go? Events made it evident to my father that Holmes knew the Professor's destination. Holmes had been in the Professor's rooms on three occasions and run through his papers. He told Watson that he had discovered nothing compromising, which was probably true, but the papers he examined may have put him on the scent of his six banking accounts which in turn, may have helped him to discover that his chief of staff, Colonel Sebastian Moran, was paid £6,000 per annum, and that he had bought a refuge in a small hamlet called Rosenlaui in the Bernese Oberland to which he retired to do much of his planning. Undoubtedly this would be his destination.

Rosenlaui would also be the near destination of Holmes and Watson and it is believed that Holmes, who had only just returned from the Continent, had made a reconnaissance of the terrain and selected the nearby Reichenbach Falls as the ideal spot for his dark deed and Meiringen as his own point of departure for the Falls.

Holmes decided that he and Watson must start their journey on the same train as my uncle in order to confirm that this deduction was correct. This would make it necessary for Holmes to be disguised and his success in the rôle of an Italian priest is described by Watson. Provided the Professor did put in an appearance Holmes could point to this as evidence that the Professor was pursuing him. Watson had never met the Professor so he was in no danger of recognition.

Holmes' deductions had so often gone astray where Professor Moriarty was concerned that he must have suffered pangs of chagrin as the clock's hands at Victoria Station arrived at the time of departure. Any anxiety he felt was explicable by his assumed fear of pursuit, but at the very last moment, he must have experienced great relief on seeing the Professor's tall figure pushing furiously forward in an attempt to catch the train.

Professor Moriarty had at least tried to catch the train and Holmes now deduced that he would engage a special train (a much easier task then than now) in order to catch the boat, or, as Holmes explained it to Watson, to catch them on the boat.

Did Watson still having lingering doubts about his friend's story when he said: 'One would think we were the criminals'? How prophetic! Or when, once again, Holmes refused to have the Professor arrested lest the smaller fish should escape arrest on the Monday, despite Holmes' belief, expressed to Watson, that the Professor would go on to Paris? 'On Monday we should have them all' he had said only a moment earlier. How could even Watson be expected to swallow this if the Professor himself was once allowed to proceed to Paris?

Holmes and Watson alighted at Canterbury and Holmes had the satisfaction of seeing that Professor Moriarty had in fact engaged a special train and would catch the boat. Now he and Watson could afford to make a leisurely and haphazard approach to their destination at Meiringen. Watson did not know they had any planned destination because, when he had asked Holmes where they were going, the reply had been 'Oh anywhere. It's all the same to me.' It was true Holmes did not much mind where they went on their way to Meiringen. The more haphazard the journey, the more convinced Watson would be that the Professor had succeeded in pursuing them.

It would be interesting to know what Watson thought two days later when Holmes with a 'bitter curse' announced that Scotland Yard had failed to arrest Professor Moriarty! 'Of course, when I left the country,' he said, 'there was no one to cope with him.' How could Watson be expected to take Holmes' remark seriously? According to Holmes' story it was his own flight to the Continent which had caused the Professor to leave England in pursuit, with Holmes' knowledge and without any attempt being made by Holmes to stop him. Whatever Watson thought, can you have any doubt that he was trying to deceive Watson?

After arriving at Meiringen by a leisurely and haphazard route, Holmes set in motion the rest of his carefully prepared plan.

My father heard later that a message had been sent in his name to his brother, Professor Moriarty, at Rosenlaui to tell him that he (my father) had arrived from London with news of the utmost importance. The message went on to say that as my father wished neither to be seen with him nor to risk disclosing his refuge in Rosenlaui by coming there, he begged him to meet him at the nearby Reichenbach Falls where they could talk unobserved and with their words drowned by the sound of the rushing waters.

I should explain that, although my father disapproved of his brother's criminal activities, they retained a close brotherly affection for each other so it would not have been at all unlikely that my father would come to his assistance in a time of crisis.

Having done this Holmes engaged a guide to take him and Watson to the Reichenbach Falls at a time which would enable them to reach the Falls about an hour before the Professor was due to arrive there.

We all know that Holmes possessed great skill in disguising himself and I shall show that, in the course of events which followed, he adopted at least a rough resemblance to my father on no less than three occasions. Although he had never met my father, who closely resembled the Professor, he had doubtless studied the full-length photograph of him which was displayed in the latter's sitting room during his three visits to the Professor's rooms. In this guise he sought out the guide once more and persuaded him with a princely bribe to leave the gentleman (Holmes) at Reichenbach Falls at some precise time (probably half an hour before the Professor was due). As part of the bargain the guide must hide himself away in some neighbouring village for a week in order to avoid a reprimand from the hotel manager until after 'the gentleman' had left the district.

Exact timing was the essence of Holmes' detailed plan and, probably just after the party of three had got out of sight of the hotel, Holmes must have turned back on some excuse, telling Watson he would catch him up. Before Holmes reached the hotel he had donned his Moriarty disguise for the second time in order to speak to the landlord. He had previously written a letter to Watson on hotel paper begging him to return to minister to a dying Englishwoman. The writing did not resemble his own and was apparently signed by the landlord. This he handed to the landlord in an envelope addressed to Watson with the request that he should find some village lad to bear it to Watson at the Reichenbach Falls as soon as possible.

Having done this, Holmes left the hotel and hurried after Watson, removing the disguise as he went.

The messenger found them at the Reichenbach Falls and Watson naturally returned to Meiringen on his errand of mercy only to find that the message was bogus. The landlord's description of the man who had left the message left no doubt in Watson's mind that he was Professor Moriarty and with fear at his heart he hastened back to the Falls, taking about two hours to reach it.

Soon after Watson had left Holmes, the Swiss guide also left Holmes on some pretext, and Holmes wasted no time in disguising himself as my father for the third time. Professor Moriarty was due in about half an hour and Watson could not get back in under about two and a half hours so the time schedule had worked out satisfactorily.

When at last Holmes saw the tall, unathletic figure of my uncle approaching, still clad in the frock coat he had been wearing when they had met ten days earlier in Baker Street, he turned away from him and very slowly moved further along the narrow path bordering the precipice. This was in order to reduce the risk of too early recognition of his true identity. He waited until the Professor was within a few paces and then turned sharply and sprang.

My uncle was a frail man several years older than Holmes and he had been taken completely by surprise. Holmes, on the other hand, was a fit man, a boxer of repute and an expert in baritsu. He had rehearsed his attack carefully in his mind and there was no desperate struggle such as Holmes described to Watson three years later. Holmes was never in danger. Grasping an outflung wrist in one hand he seized the same arm above the elbow with his other hand, gave a violent twist and sent my uncle spinning over the precipice. Down he fell for a long way, 'then he struck a rock, bounded off, and splashed into the water'.

The perfect murder? The accidental death, it would be said, of the sinister criminal who had sworn vengeance, who had made several attempts on his life and who had tracked him across Europe. The subtle manner in which the Professor had isolated Holmes from his companions in order to make a murderous attack on him would be noted. In the course of the struggle Holmes had miraculously escaped whilst the Professor himself had fallen to his doom. Holmes would not only be absolved from all blame. He would be congratulated.

No, it was not the perfect murder! Just one little miscalculation prevented this from being the end of the story.

Whilst Holmes had been setting fire to 221B Baker Street, Professor Moriarty had also been busy. For a handsome fee he had bribed an innocent man to take the place of Colonel Sebastian Moran for three days whilst the Colonel made good his escape to Rosenlaui by a different route. The substitution had not been easy and this is what had caused Professor Moriarty to miss his train at Victoria.

The innocent substitute had been arrested on the Monday and the mistake had only been discovered by the police after they had telegraphed to Holmes that all the gang had been arrested except the Professor himself. Holmes' 'bitter curse' would have been genuine if he had known that the most dangerous member of the gang was at liberty.

Although Professor Moriarty thought the message he had received from his brother was genuine, his customary caution persuaded him to send Colonel Moran on in advance to the mountain slope on the further side of the Falls from which he could see if the meeting was a trap and signal if necessary to the Professor before he arrived. Moran's route was a difficult one and by the time he arrived Holmes was already alone. Moran did not know my father but he could see a solitary figure bearing a resemblance to the Professor so he had no grounds for suspicion.

With mounting horror Moran was a witness to the murder. He also saw Holmes strip off his disguise and fling it after my uncle's body into the cauldron of waters beneath him. Even from the distance which separated them he could recognize Sherlock Holmes. After calculating that a difficult traverse along the steep mountain slope might enable him to cut off Holmes' retreat down the valley, he sprang to his feet, dislodged a boulder in his haste and was seen by Holmes.

Now it was Holmes' turn to take rapid stock of the serious position in which he found himself and to rearrange his plans to meet the dangers which beset him. Rapidly he wrote the message to Watson which is faithfully recorded in *The Final Problem* and managed to clamber to a ledge where he could lie concealed both from Moran and from the search party led by Watson. Here he had time to work out his plans of action. He was certainly faced with what he would have described as 'a three-pipe' problem but with no chance of lighting a pipe for fear of giving away his place of concealment.

Subsequent events suggest that Holmes argued along the following lines:

1. He was in grave danger of death from Colonel Moran who, though apparently unarmed at present, was a notable big game hunter and crack shot. He was credited with the worst of crimes in the service of Professor Moriarty and would do his best to avenge his murder.

2. He was in grave danger of a murder charge being brought against him. Nevertheless he could count on Moran trying to hunt him down in preference to bringing a charge against him because he, Moran himself, was liable to be arrested on charges of murder and other serious offences in most countries of Europe.

3. His letter to Watson coupled with his complete disap-

pearance would convince Watson and the local police that he
and Professor Moriarty had both perished and he must leave
Watson in the dark until he had achieved a satisfactory solution. This would take time. The solution could lie in his win-
ning the duel between Moran and himself. That would mean
another murder on his hands. Or in pinning a murder charge
on Moran. Should the latter prove possible he might be able to
make a bargain with Moran—his own safety in return for that
of Holmes. Time alone could provide his final solution but in
the meantime he must remain 'dead'.

4. If Watson published the dramatic story of his death,
Colonel Moriarty would certainly publish a denial. He might
do this in any case and allege murder against Holmes after
getting Moran's eye-witness account but, as Moran could not
afford to appear in person, there was a good chance that Colonel
Moriarty would refrain from doing this, at present at any rate,
in the hope that Moran would succeed in hunting him down and
avenging the Professor's death.

5. He (Holmes) must take one man into his confidence at the
earliest possible opportunity—his brother Mycroft Holmes—
and we know he did this. He must understand his double danger,
of being murdered by Moran or being sent to the gallows for
murder. Mycroft must prevent Watson publishing anything and
likewise use his great influence to prevent my father (Colonel
Moriarty) from publishing anything. Mycroft must supply him
with funds during his period of hiding and retain his quarters at
221B Baker Street.

6. Although he (Holmes) must be ever watchful, he must try
to keep Moran on his trail. It must be a prolonged game of
hide and seek where the hunter's interest is retained, and where
the hunter may in the end suffer defeat himself. Holmes needed
time.

Moran's attempt to ambush Holmes on his way down the
valley did not meet with success because Holmes was lying
concealed on his ledge. Moran waited. He saw Watson come
and then go with grief written across his face. Moran knew
Holmes had not followed the tracks either to Meiringen or to
Rosenlaui so he must still be somewhere on the mountain slope.
Careful search was interrupted later by officials from Meiringen
so he had to wait until they were gone. Not until the evening

did he at last see a solitary figure silhouetted on a distant sky-line.

Days extended into weeks with Moran still trailing Holmes. His appetite was whetted by clues to Holmes' whereabouts, some genuine, and others sham whenever he came too close. Then he learned with indignation that the local authorities had brought in a verdict in accordance with Watson's testimony shortly after receiving news that Holmes had made his way into Italy. Before pursuing him there Moran returned to Meiringen to make a full statement. Moran did not hear until years later that Meiringen was virtually wiped out by fire shortly after-wards. So devastating were the flames that hardly a house re-mained standing. Surely this was no coincidence? We have al-ways assumed that Holmes started this fire as he had started one in Baker Street a few weeks earlier. By this means he de-stroyed all evidence against himself and created a diversion which prevented Moran's version of the story being investi-gated.

In the end, alas, things turned out exactly as Holmes had planned. He kept Moran on his trail for a prolonged period. Eventually my father's hopes vanished of Moran avenging his brother so he decided to publish the true story, only to find that Moran refused to come forward to give evidence and that no publisher in Britain dared to publish the unsupported story. Nor would the police take him seriously. His impotence en-raged him, especially when Watson, fearing he might find a publisher, got Mycroft Holmes' permission to publish his version in *The Final Problem* in 1893.

Neither Holmes' friends nor his enemies have readily accepted Holmes' later story of visits to Mecca and Tibet and it is much more probable that he lurked in Europe, after finding the game of hide and seek was no longer profitable, and kept himself informed of Colonel Moran's activities in the hope of being able to pounce on him at the right moment.

Through Mycroft Holmes he probably prevailed on the police to drop their charges against Moran with the result that in due time Holmes found himself in the position he had hoped for, namely to convict him of the murder of Ronald Adair in London.

Holmes had three objectives, only the first of which was

known to anybody but himself at the time! He wanted Colonel Moran arrested once he (Holmes) could have him convicted of the murder of Ronald Adair. Secondly, he planned to capture him whilst using his unique air-gun. This would add to the evidence against him but, beyond this, it would ensure its confiscation and that was vital to Holmes whose dread of this weapon was genuine. Thirdly, having had him arrested and his gun confiscated, Holmes planned to negotiate with Moran. The bargain he intended to strike was that his evidence leading to Moran's conviction for murder would be withheld if Moran would cease his vendetta against him and 'forget' what he had seen at Reichenbach Falls. He achieved all these objectives.

Let us notice a few significant points in Watson's story of Moran's arrest.

Holmes had many friendly contacts with the underworld and it cannot be doubted that through devious channels Holmes made it known to Moran that he would be visiting Baker Street, perhaps only for one night, in order to collect some of his possessions before going into hiding again. The trap was set to arrest Moran when firing his air-gun at the wax model of Sherlock Holmes in the window of 221B.

Now look at the remarks made by Colonel Moran and Inspector Lestrade when they met Holmes in the empty house opposite 221B. 'You cunning, cunning fiend,' said Moran and how fully he must have meant those words after all that passed between them. 'It's good to see you back in London, sir,' said Lestrade. Here the words ring strangely as a welcome back from the grave after three years during which period all except Mycroft Holmes had believed him to be dead. The explanation must have lain in Mycroft telling Scotland Yard that Holmes was still alive but that for his own safety and success in hunting down the remains of the Moriarty gang it was essential for his survival to be kept a secret.

After Colonel Moran was arrested in the empty house it is interesting to notice how keen Holmes was not to figure in the case. He flatly refused to allow Lestrade to charge Moran with the attempted murder of himself which the police had witnessed themselves. 'I do not propose to appear in the matter at all,' he said.

It would not have suited him to have any publicity at this

stage, especially in view of the bargain he intended to make with Moran which would cover safety from attack or charges by Moran's associates, including my father.

Moran was not convicted of murder, as we all know, and Holmes was neither attacked nor charged by Professor Moriarty's associates and relations from that time onwards, despite my father's rage at this turn of events. Nevertheless Holmes was wise enough not to allow Watson to publish the case of *The Empty House* until after my father's death and his own retirement to a secret refuge, which none has discovered, somewhere in the Sussex Downs. This was in 1903.

Sir Arthur Conan Doyle records that 'a witty critic' remarked 'He [Sherlock Holmes] may not have been killed when he fell over the cliff, but he was never quite the same man afterwards.' There is many a true word spoken in jest! Was it conscience or a lingering fear of exposure which affected him?

Moran is dead, my father is dead, and I am not bound by any blackmailing bargain struck by Holmes in 1894. Nor am I scared of his bringing a libel action against me because that would seal his doom.

Yours sincerely,

JAMES MORIARTY

❧ * 16 * ❧

LORD DONEGALL

APRIL 1891–APRIL 1894

April is a bumper month for Sherlockian students. By a happy coincidence, the action in both of the Heavenly Twins—my own name for *The Final Problem* and *The Empty House*—starts in April, respectively 1891 and 1894.

Although anything but identical, these 'twins' are complementary. They enable us to consider the events leading up to The Great Hiatus or Holmes' *Wanderjahre*—as that supreme expert on the subject, A. Carson Simpson, of the Sons of the Copper Beeches, Philadelphia, has called the three years, ten months and three weeks period of the great detective's supposed death—together with the events subsequent to his dramatic reappearance in London.

In *The Final Problem*, Professor James Moriarty, the Napoleon of Crime 'for ever slowly oscillating from side to side in a curiously reptilian fashion', makes his first appearance, although Holmes has apparently been on his tail for years and the net is ready to close on the principal members of his vast criminal organization. (It is curious, in view of the fact that Dr Watson *had* heard of Moriarty in *The Valley of Fear* (1887), that he professes *never* to have heard of him in *The Final Problem* (1891).)

After dodging a two-horse van, missing a brick on his head and avoiding a rough with a bludgeon, Holmes decides that a little relaxation on the Continent would be better for his health. The ever-mobile doctor announces a 'quiet practice and an accommodating neighbour'.

Now, about three-and-a-half pages earlier, Watson quotes Holmes as stating categorically that 'by Monday next, the Professor, with *all* the principal members of his gang, will be in the hands of the police'. The destruction of Moriarty and his minions being the culmination of his career up to that moment, one would have presumed that Holmes would hardly go off on a jaunt, giving Inspector Lestrade and his like every opportunity to bungle the whole operation.

Indeed, Holmes must have anticipated a slip-up because he gets Watson to send his luggage to Paris (where they have no intention of going), tells him not to take the first two cabs available to Victoria and expresses no surprise when he sees Professor Moriarty miss the boat-train. He has even gone so far as to disguise himself as an Italian priest, a piece of play-acting that seems hardly necessary if Moriarty is 100 per cent certain to be in the bag by Monday.

'Ah, there is Moriarty himself!' says Holmes, casually, as the Professor makes vain efforts to catch the train.

Now we come to the Remarkable Special (British Rail please note!). The boat-train might be expected, supposing that it averaged 50 m.p.h., to take about 1 hour 13 minutes from Victoria to Canterbury, where our travellers cunningly alight and hide behind a pile of luggage to watch Moriarty's Special Train, consisting of a locomotive and a carriage, roar by, *one minute later*.

Let us suppose that this amazing train averaged 75 m.p.h. from Victoria to Canterbury, without coming off the rails; the station master at Victoria Station must have been a superorganizer with a staff trained to the standards of the London Fire Brigade. It appears to have taken him only twelve minutes to organize a Special, clear the line to Canterbury, get the train alongside an empty platform and send it on its way. (I suggest that, nowadays, it would have taken Moriarty longer than that to fill in the necessary forms, in triplicate.)

Somewhat belatedly, Holmes sagely remarks: 'I might have known it. He has escaped!'

For years, there was much argument among Sherlockian Bradshaw experts about the plausibility of Holmes and Watson making their connections from Canterbury to Newhaven, in time to catch the packet steamer *Paris* (belonging to the London, Brighton and South Coast Railway) to Dieppe. In 1891, she was the last thing in 'confort moderne': steel-built, electrically lighted, with luxury cabins, making the crossing in 5½ hours.

But it has now been definitely established through the laborious researches of Mr Bernard Davies (*Sherlock Holmes Journal*, Vol. 5, No. 2) that, via Ashford Junction, a slow train to Hastings, changing again for Lewes, they would have reached Newhaven at 3.45 p.m. By consulting Bradshaw's Continental Railway, Steam Navigation and Conveyance Guide (1891), it is simple (always supposing that you have one handy) to ascertain that, via Rouen (change at 5.41 a.m.), then Amiens, Valenciennes and Mons, they would have reached Brussels at 6 p.m. the following evening (Sunday), with their luggage irrevocably impounded at the Gare du Nord, in Paris.

The remainder of our travellers' roundabout journey to the little Swiss village of Meiringen is uneventful until they climb up to the Reichenbach Falls, that 'shaft into which the river hurls itself; an immense chasm . . . boiling pit of incalculable depth. . . .'

Watson having been lured away for a bogus patient, Moriarty turns up and, we are informed, Holmes and the Professor 'locked in each other's arms' plunge into that 'dreadful cauldron of swirling water and seething foam'.

And that, as far as the *Strand* magazine was concerned, was the end of him of whom Watson (doubtless knowing his Plato's *Phaedo* by heart) says: 'I shall ever regard him as the best and the wisest man whom I have ever known.'

It is not until ten years later that admirers of Mr Holmes learn of The Great Hiatus, when Sir Arthur Conan Doyle releases *The Empty House* to the *Strand* magazine for October 1903.

In April 1894, the murder, at his Park Lane house, of the Honourable Ronald Adair, second son of the Earl of Maynooth, after playing whist at the Bagatelle Club, caused Holmes to return to London from Montpelier (where he had been researching into coal-tar derivatives), send Watson into the first and last faint he ever had in his life and dispose (though he was unaccountably not hanged) of Colonel Sebastian Moran (Eton and Oxford)—'the best heavy game shot that our Eastern Empire has ever produced . . . the most dangerous man in London'.

Apart from the fact that Holmes suspected Moran of Adair's murder, he was justifiably annoyed with this right-hand man of the late Professor Moriarty. Moran, having carelessly left his famous German air-gun somewhere, had showered boulders down on Holmes just after he had contrived not to fall into the Reichenbach chasm with the Professor.

Several experts have been at unworthy pains to label Holmes' long account to Watson of his wanderings during the three years of The Great Hiatus as a 'cock-and-bull' story. They ridicule the idea that Holmes disguised himself as Sigerson, a Norwegian explorer, and travelled for two years in Tibet, visiting Lhassa and spending some days with the Head Lama.

Of course, Holmes' statement that he paid an interesting visit to the Khalifa at Khartoum is palpable nonsense. But it does not necessarily invalidate all the rest. Khartoum was destroyed in 1885, and, in 1893–4, the Khalifa was in Omdurman, where Holmes may have visited him and, as he asserts, communicated the results to the Foreign Office.

Mr A. Carson Simpson holds that Watson confused Khartoum with Kharta, an administrative district of Tibet: 'I visited the Khalifa and Kharta.'

Mr Simpson may well be right, especially as this explanation serves to strengthen Holmes' account of his Tibetan explorations.

Doubt has also been cast on the whole of the Tibetan journey on the grounds,

(*a*) that he could not have entered Tibet, much less have got near Lhassa or the Dalai Lama, and
(*b*) that he could not possibly have done the return journey, *and* travelled two years in Tibet, in the time available.

In 1891, it was undoubtedly difficult for a foreigner to gain access to Tibet. But there were four major expeditions in Tibet —two English, one American and one French—between 1891 and 1894. No European had reached Lhassa since 1846, when Fathers Huc and Gabet left the city.

We must remember, however, that Mycroft Holmes, at the Foreign Office, 'occasionally *is* the British Government', and was in a position to obtain unique facilities for his brother. It is undoubtedly because of Russia's intrigues on the North West Frontier, at the time, and the consequent strained relations with Britain (see Kipling's *The Truce of the Bear*), that Mycroft arranged, through the King of Scandinavia, to whom Holmes rendered singular services, for his brother to be issued with a

Norwegian passport and the identity of a parson. (That eminent authority on British customs, N. Coward, has pointed out that only mad dogs and Englishmen go out in the mid-day sun. This may have slightly restricted Holmes' activities and travel during the siesta hours, lest he reveal his true nationality.)

We have the authority of Sir Charles Bell, for many years British Representative in Tibet, for the phrase 'Head Lama'. Denigrators of Holmes have, in their ignorance, leapt at the conclusion that he referred to the Dalai Lama. A minimum of research would have shown that the Dalai Lama was a minor. The Regent, who was abbot of the great monastery of Ten-gyeling, was known as the Head Lama. Furthermore, he was combating Russian influence over his ward and was, therefore, susceptible to British approaches.

The whole Mycroft–Foreign Office–Holmes operation now begins to make sense, and, in view of the highest-level international implications, the 'some days in Lhassa with the Head Lama' loses all its improbability.

It would take up too much space to prove, in full detail, that, with the means of travel available between 1891 and 1894, Holmes could have been entirely truthful in his account to Watson of his *Wanderjahre*.

Briefly, if you work it all out, Holmes is left with ten months and three weeks for his travelling (apart from the two years in Tibet) or, eight months for his journey from Florence to Tibet and back to Montpelier, in Southern France.

We have no details of his eastward journey and must presume that he went by Royal Mail to Bombay and on by rail to Darjeeling. He could have reached Tibet in twenty-five to thirty days. He must have returned by land, leaving Tibet by Chinese Turkestan, avoiding troubled Afghanistan.

If Holmes used a map, it has not yet come into any collector's possession. Maps of Tibet are to be found as early as 1798, in the Hsi-chao-t'u lüeh. But the Chinese believed the earth to be flat, that China was in the middle of it and that compass needles pointed to south.

Holmes probably thought that such a map—with north at the bottom of it—might tend to confuse Dr Watson.

By caravan, this thousand-mile trip, at the pace of twenty miles a day, as achieved by the 1904 Younghusband Expedition, would take fifty days to Samarkand. Then, the Transcaspian Railway and caravan to Basra, occupying another sixty-two days. Allowing for the 'look-in at Mecca' and crossing the Red Sea, we must allocate Holmes another fifty-five days, partly up the White Nile, to arrive at his meeting with the Khalifa, at Omdurman. Another eighteen days to Wady Halfa and ten from there to Montpelier.

So it will be seen that, allowing for some minor delays, Holmes took seven months from Tibet to Montpelier. Add this to the twenty-five days of the eastward journey, and he is still within the eight months postulated for his eastward and westward journeys combined.

Q.E.D.

BERNARD DAVIES

THE BACK YARDS OF BAKER STREET

' . . . *None the less you must come round to my view, for otherwise I shall keep piling fact upon fact on you, until your reason breaks down under them and acknowledges me to be right. . . .*' The Red-Headed League.

I was reminded of the perennial fascination of the mystery of 221B, over which the tides of ink rise higher year by year, by a perusal of James Edward Holroyd's delightful birthday book for unbelievers—*Baker Street By-ways*. We are by now accustomed to this author's genial virtues, not the least of which is an admirable breadth of mind. To the one topic on which Mr Holroyd may be said to have something of an *idée fixe* he appends this comment: 'How reassuring it would be in this Conan Doyle centenary year if the precise position of 221B could be established, like good old Watson himself, as "the one fixed point in a changing age" . . . ' It is a sentiment we warm to, even if we detect the faint hint that he would welcome any solution providing it was No 109!

Holmes' own centenary has come and gone with no less than three commemorative plaques to mark its passing. Yet Baker Street, the very heartland of Holmes' London, bears no tribute to its most illustrious inhabitant. It is a sobering thought. Few Sherlockians would hasten the day when all the obscurities of the Canon are made plain to them. But surely here is an exception, the one mystery we should all wish to solve, if only to avoid that acute embarrassment when asked to point out the home of Holmes. What can we say on such occasions? That 'each may form his own hypothesis upon the present evidence and yours is as likely to be correct as mine'?

Ever since Dr Gray Chandler Briggs threw down the scholarly

gauntlet many years ago the fight has waxed fast and furious up and down Baker Street. Wielding pin-pricks of delicate inference as if they were bludgeons, theorists have laid about them and demolished each other's cherished structures in turn. Each cut deep, but his successor just undercut him, while at intervals a new shrine arose beside the rubble of the old.

The inevitable reaction followed:—the emergence of serious doubts as to whether 221B was really in Baker Street, W.1, at all. It does not surprise us that this heresy (amongst others) should first see light in the United States, where a taste for strange theologies is, so to speak, endemic, but the conception that the immortal rooms were in Gloucester Place, because it more closely resembles the Baker Street of Holmes' day, is at once repugnant and erroneous. As for Mr Michael Harrison's Brixton red herrings, we can only ascribe them to a perverse desire to be difficult and class them with his other discovery: that Moriarty chartered his special from the South-Eastern Railway because he preferred their first-class accommodation to that of the London, Chatham and Dover! His brother being a station-master, no doubt he had a fine taste in such things.

Any investigator rash enough to open the case afresh might well exclaim: 'If a herd of buffaloes had passed along there could not be a greater mess!' My own ideas, however, developed slowly during the years in which I was engaged in formulating principles for topographical detection which, while they did not exclude the logical use of inference, placed it firmly on a basis of detailed map-work and research in the field. It was at a much later stage, when these principles were applied to the meagre indications of the text, that one thing became plain. Baker Street had previously been shrouded in a fog of irrelevancy thicker than anything in the pages of Watson. It is to dispel that fog that the story of 'The Back Yards of Baker Street' has been written, a story for which I am confident the Sherlockian world is more than prepared.

Contrary to the beliefs of Gloucester Place theorists Baker Street has not greatly changed since Holmes' day. Unlike the Strand, its spacious building lines have never been altered while new blocks have only intruded here and there. Trade invaded its quiet in the 'sixties with the opening of the Metropolitan station and by the 'eighties it was firmly established from Portman Square to Paddington Street, where the old basement areas had largely (though not entirely) disappeared. Sometimes the lower windows remained, sometimes they were replaced by shop-fronts, many of which retain their Victorian aspect to this day.

The fact that York Place and Upper Baker Street remained predominantly residential until much later has created some prejudice against siting 221B in the lower reaches. Yet there is not a word in the saga which is inimical to such a solution. The street frontage is never described nor is any reference made to the premises below the famous sitting-room. Most of these houses, on leaseholds from the Portman Estate, were sublet on divided leases and there is no valid reason why No 221A, the ground-floor front (with possibly the basement), should not have been occupied as a shop or office quite distinct from Mrs Hudson's establishment, 221B.

That settled, let us briefly examine the credentials of some of the popular theories which, as Mr Holroyd points out, fall into three main groups. Dr Gray Briggs of course plumped solidly for Group (b) with No 111 in Upper York Place and its opposite number, Camden House School, at No 118. 'No more brilliant identification has been made in our time,' as Vincent Starrett put it. No more unfortunate would be a better description, seeing that Dr Briggs' blindness to the true *desiderata* has all too plainly been passed on to later writers. The main objection to this thesis is, of course, that David Mews (formerly York Mews North) at the rear of No 118 can only be reached from a passage off Blandford Street by means of a tortuous detour for which there is absolutely no warranty in the text.

In Group (a), north of the station, the Fundamental or 'Holmes-without-Tears' School stick to the now demolished No 221 and perpetuate the quaint fiction that Holmes happily anticipated renumbering by some thirty years, at the same time leading Watson blindfold from Blandford Street across Marylebone Road without the latter realizing it! However much we may admire the assiduity with which the Abbey National Building Society cope with the great detective's not inconsiderable mail, we should not let this blind us to realities.

In Group (c) at the opposite pole, the strained semantics of Dr Maurice Campbell (No 27) and the dubious topography of

Mr James Hyslop (No 19) have been dealt with by Mr Holroyd in a suitably cavalier fashion. North of Blandford Street the late Gavin Brend selected Nos 59–63, making his principal points perhaps a shade too fine. It is unfortunate that Mr Michael Harrison accepts this siting unresefvedly, despite the fact, which he himself had previously demonstrated, that in the 'eighties Mr Brend's Nos 59–63 were Nos 56, 57 and 58 and were occupied (among other ventures) by the frontage of the vast Baker Street Bazaar, the Portman Rooms, Druce's upholstery works, and a carriage repository!

So banishing the sneaking feeling that if 221B had been anywhere but in the original Baker Street, Watson would have said so, we return to York Place and Mr Holroyd's No 109.

This was the brain-child of Mr Ernest Short who selected No 108, the present YWCA hostel, as *The Empty House*. Mr Holroyd agreed to take the case and has supported it with a veritable barrage of argument, much of it shrewd. He earns our undying gratitude for reducing to its proper size that common denominator of existing theories—the interpretation of vague and chameleon-like English prepositions. He has, above all, freed us from the tyranny of the Bank, the Station, the Tobacconist, the Post Office, Old Uncle Alex Holder and All. He has, in short, cut out the unmitigated bleat.

But Mr Holroyd's crusade is not without its own pitfalls. In *The Resident Patient* he argues that Holmes and Watson must have been taking the shortest way home from the Hanover Square end of Brook Street and that therefore to go 'half-way down Harley Street' before turning west must have carried them into the latitude of York Place and No 109. Herein lies a fallacy, and although we cannot muster the canonical seven other explanations of this passage, we can submit five.

1. They were *not* taking the shortest way home. Even from Hanover Square, the New Bond Street-Marylebone Lane route is at least one eighth of a mile shorter, to No 109 or anywhere else in Baker Street. 'It is a capital mistake. . . .' Need we go on?

2. They turned off nearly half-way at New Cavendish Street, not a great diversion as it enters the High Street only twenty-five yards above Blandford Street.

3. Watson was thinking in terms of 'half-way northward' from Oxford Street to Marylebone Road.

4. Holmes was walking in abstracted and irritated silence and they overshot their turning.

5, and most likely. Watson merely meant 'some way up Harley Street'. Can we imagine he measured it? In such a context it is just as absurdly hair-splitting to take 'half-way' literally as it is the 'down' in 'down the street'. The word is mere colloquial hyperbole.

But Mr Holroyd glories chiefly in what we may call 'The Abracadabra School': a massive array of numerological contortions purporting to reveal the mystic solution '109'. Figures, of course, can be made to reveal almost anything if enough liberty is taken with them and, as Senior Wrangler, Mr Holroyd has plenty of leeway. Not content with this, he conducts cabalistic researches into the text, unearthing secret (if Irregular) cyphers, and sees signs and wonders, not in the heavens, but in the ground-plan of the Portman Estate. This *tour de force*, he claims, follows the imperishable doctrine on 'the observance of trifles'. 'But are we to give serious attention to such things? This agency stands flat-footed upon the ground, and there it must remain.'

John H. Watson had neither the subtlety of mind nor the accuracy with figures for indulging in elaborate cryptograms. We may suspect him of being an erstwhile Tractarian—but never a Rosicrucian. It is regrettable that amid all this rune-casting Watson's more solid virtues should go, as always, unnoticed. Straightforward rather than devious, he was above all a good reporter and what he has left us is there for the winnowing. Trifles, it is true—but trifles of cold, hard fact.

It is time to employ them; time to abandon those sterile and discredited theories based on verbal quibbling, those sketchy estimates of position that have produced nothing but a succession of worthless claimants whose credentials do not bear looking into. Let us rely instead on Watson's unmistakable references to the physical characteristics of the houses themselves.

We may list the following essential requirements for the two buildings:

(A) THE EMPTY HOUSE

BACK. 1. It must have had a mews or similar passage

behind it giving access to the rear premises. *No house without one can be accepted.*

2. It must have possessed a back yard abutting on to this mews. As the back door opened into this yard the latter must have been an *open space at the rear*, not a small enclosed court or air-well within the building.

3. Holmes and Watson passed 'through a wooden gate' from the mews into the yard, therefore there was no mews property intervening.

FRONT. 4. Its front door and entrance-hall must have been on the *south* side (i.e. on the *right* when viewed from the street). 'Holmes turned suddenly to the right' into the front room when approaching from the rear, impossible if the hall was on the north.

5. There was no street-lamp outside it in 1894. 'There was no lamp near . . . '

(B) 221B

BACK. 1. It must have possessed a back yard large enough to contain a plane tree at the time of *Thor Bridge* (*circa* 1900). The tree may not have been very large but the October wind 'whirling the last remaining leaves' from its branches suggests that it was of reasonable height and foliage. The yard, therefore, was fairly spacious and open to the wind. Both factors, together with the phrase, 'behind our house', rule out a narrow well or court within the building.

FRONT. 2. Here there are numerous points, but none of any practical use: (a) 'Two large windows' in the sitting room. Few Baker Street houses are only two windows width across, but we cannot be certain how far across the frontage the room extended at that period. (b) One was a 'bow-window'. At no time does any house appear to have had such a window. This is dubious and may be a literary fancy. At best, it was probably an ephemeral device. (c) At least three storeys high, as Watson slept on a floor above. All the original buildings have at least three floors. (d) The front door possessed a semicircular fanlight. This, in some form, was practically universal. (e) The main staircase had seventeen steps up to the first landing. My own researches confirm those of Dr W. S. Bristowe. All existing examples have about twenty, some more. No 109 has twenty-five!

(a) and (b) are so doubtful, (c) and (d) so universal, while (e) is so in conflict with the known facts that it is advisable to ignore the front elevation entirely and rely solely on Point (1).

Now to the map. In this respect Sherlockians owe a great debt to the Ordnance Survey. All our data concerning *The Empty House* relates to the year 1894 and it was in this and the preceding year that they undertook the re-surveying of the 5 foot to 1 mile plans of London, first published in the 'seventies. For our purpose anything other than contemporary material (even if only approximately so) is virtually useless. Published in 1895, the 2nd Edition Sheets VII/41 and 51 show Baker Street *exactly* as it was at the time of *The Empty House*.

With these maps before us, let us first appraise the value and limitations of certain evidence.

1. The Passage, and 2. The Yard are unassailable, and there can be no exceptions to them.

3. The Gate. Here we strike a difficulty. From the map it is obvious that the only yards opening *directly* out of the mews passages east of Baker Street are a few near the entries, all of them belonging to houses in streets running *across* Baker Street. No houses *in* Baker Street possessed such yards. In every case some stable or similar building lay between the yard and the passage. We must accept this as fact. Watson must have omitted to mention that they passed through some mews premises to reach the yard.

4. The Front Doors. The positions of these are only indicated on our maps by the basement areas marked as remaining. Where, as was so frequently the case, these had been paved or grated over we must repair the deficiency by careful field work. In all the blocks not rebuilt the position of the original halls and stairways can clearly be seen. Some can be checked by reference to the earlier 1st Edition maps of 1872, when more areas still remained. This data is accordingly entered on the accompanying map. A greater drawback is that so many houses *have* their doors on the south that it is difficult to eliminate a great number of houses. It is therefore advisable to use this only as a secondary factor, in order to eliminate buildings which might qualify on other grounds.

5. The Street-lamps. These were marked on the 1st Edition, 1872, but were unfortunately omitted from the 2nd Edition. Our information thus relates to a period some twenty years earlier. Old photographs of Baker Street, while they show some improvements in lighting by the 'nineties, also show that these were in the main confined to multiplication of lamps at the principal crossings and junctions. While the erection of possible odd lamps in other stretches is not ruled out, there is no sign of any general *rearrangement* prior to the introduction of the modern electric standards. Lamps shown on the 1872 map can be seen in the same positions many years later and it can be taken for granted that any house shown as having a lamp outside it in the 'seventies also had one outside it in the 'nineties. This data is likewise shown on our working map. But the problem is to decide how near to a lamp a house could stand without being disqualified. At least one house-width away would seem a reasonable minimum, but as the sitings vary in relation to the housefronts, it is probably advisable to employ this too as a secondary factor, and then only to rule out otherwise suitable buildings which have a lamp *immediately outside*.

It naturally follows that the main burden of identification rests on Points (1) and (2), which we shall proceed to apply.

We commence by eliminating absolutely any sections of the east side disqualified on Point (1) alone. These are: (1) All Group (a)—north of the Metropolitan station (Sheet VII/41), and with them No 221 opposite. None of these houses had a passage behind them, or any rear access, either from Allsop Place or Marylebone Road. (2) Nos 126–136 York Place. (Sheet VII/51.) There was no rear mews between these houses and the newly-erected Portman Mansions. (3) The George Street-Robert Adam Street block near the bottom, no rear passage existing behind No 18 or No 20. (4) The lowest block, above Portman Square. Bakers Mews, the only passage here was entered from Baker Street itself and is quite unacceptable.

Having excluded the above from all further consideration, we are left with all the blocks between Portman Mansions and George Street, including most of York Place. (See Map on end paper.) All these had rear passages and we shall apply the same tests to all of them, whether the passages could be reached in a direct line from Blandford Street or not. However, the corner house (or houses) in each block, to which there was no access from the rear, have been omitted from the numbered groups.

Of these groups the following houses had yards at the *rear* and immediately adjoining a mews premises through which Holmes and Watson must have passed:

5. York Place: Nos 98–120. *None.* All had small internal wells. (Those at the top also had their doors on the north while Dr Brigg's No 118 had, in addition, a lamp outside the door, thus being disqualified on three counts!) The Short-Holroyd No 108 formed with No 110 a joint establishment housing the Bedford College for Women. Even if their internal yards had adjoined the mews (which they did not), they are both out of the question; No 108 because to enter its front room it would be necessary to turn *left* from the main hall; No 110 because there was a lamp right outside it! (Incidentally, the line of sight to No 109 was about fifty degrees off—tricky shooting even for an 'old shikari'!)

6. Dorset Street to Paddington Street—Nos 76–88. *Only one*, No 88, had a yard at the rear adjoining the present Kenrick Place. Others were either internal or absent altogether.

7. Blandford Street to Dorset Street, Nos 40–66. *Only one*, No 60, had a rear yard. (A very small one.) A few others possessed internal wells but most had been built over right to the present Broadstone Place, including the joint building, Nos 62–4, opposite Mr Brend's heavily occupied choice.

8. George Street to Blandford Street Nos 22–34. *Only two*, Nos 30 and 34 are suitable. (Although the 1872 map shows several large yards, these had been built over during the intervening years. There was by now no yard opposite Mr Hyslop's No 19.)

This brings us to our southern limit of search and our sum total of possibilities, Nos 88, 60, 34, and 30. Of these No 88 and No 60 can certainly be eliminated on Point (5) as they had street-lamps right outside their windows, while No 30 (alas, opposite Dr Campbell's No 27) must also be vetoed on Point (4), its door and hall-way being plainly on the north.

This leaves No 34, out of all the possible houses, likely and unlikely, the only conceivable choice for *The Empty House.*

The following interesting points are in its favour. First, its yard (about 20 ft by 6 ft) ran behind the Blandford Street houses and was entered via a curious little mews property unlike any other in the street. A small shed, hardly wider than the yard and sandwiched in between two premises of the usual size, it might easily have seemed a mere tunnel into the yard beyond and caused Watson to give the impression that no typical mews building intervened. Whether it possessed a wooden gate at this period we do not know. Also it was the first yard on the right, just inside the narrow bottleneck of the entry. This not only fits the 'narrow passage' far better than a stretch of mews nearly thirty feet wide but also accords with the strong suggestion that they reached the gate immediately after entering the passage. Lastly, the chances of a street-lamp having been erected nearer to No 34 by the 'nineties are negligible. The nearest is not too far away (about 40 feet) but far enough to shed only a faint light.

Incidentally, Gavin Brend's condemnation of a Kendalls Place solution on the grounds that Holmes would not have wasted time approaching it via Blandford Street defeats itself. Curiously enough Blandford Street *is* the quickest route from Cavendish Square to No 34 by some twenty or thirty yards. The explanation lies in the rectangular street-pattern hereabouts, which slopes west-south-west and carries anyone walking west (as to George Street) slightly away from points north. On the other hand parts of the older streets such as Marylebone Lane or South Street, now eastern Blandford Street, cut corners and sometimes run almost due west, thus saving a slight distance in walking to any but the lowest houses in this block.

Turning to the west side and the problem of 221B we find our task more straightforward, namely to select any houses which had yards at the back large enough to contain a plane tree. Even a tree that was small in 1900 would have been there in 1894 so our 2nd Edition map will suffice. It only requires a check on a later edition to ensure that such yards existed some years later. Confining our search to the numbers opposite those blocks with rear mews that we have previously examined we find the following yards:—Opposite (5) York Place—Nos 91–113. (Divided by York Street.) *None.* All those marked are small wells within the buildings. Opposite (6) Dorset Street to Crawford Street—Nos 69–89. *None.* The solitary small one at No 71 (the Bank) is internal. Opposite (7) King Street (now part of Blandford Street) to Dorset Street—Nos 37–67. *None*. Although the 1872 map shows several fair-sized yards they had all vanished under various structures by 1894, when only three small spaces are marked. That behind No 65 was only about ten feet long and narrowly waisted in the centre, while the one at No 43 (the Post Office) was even smaller. No 57 had only a tiny internal well.

Opposite (8) George Street to King Street—Nos 19–35. *Only one*—at No. 31. Five spacious yards of 1872 had been reduced to one and a couple of air-shafts. The remaining example, a space some 15 ft by 12 ft, lay behind the house overlooking King Street Mews. (Now the Milk Depot.) It stands out on the map as the only back yard in the entire street which answers the description. A glance at the survey of 1921 shows that this yard remained intact for many years. Once more the map, recording the disappearance of so many yards with the march of commerce, points with uncanny precision to the true site of 221B.

The clinching argument is, of course, as plain as a pikestaff. No 31 and No 34 are opposite each other. Not dead opposite, it is true, but near enough for the sight-line to be no more than fifteen to twenty degrees off. These two sites are interdependent in terms of the text, yet their identifications are at once independent and conclusive. Here, and nowhere else, could that famous vigil have been kept opposite that bright window in the gloom on which 'the shadow of a man who was seated on a chair within was thrown in hard, black outline—a perfect reproduction of Holmes'. Our half-mile search of Baker Street could come to no more happy and reassuring end.

What of the future? Both houses are fortunately still standing. On the ground floor No 34 is now a travel agency, in whose office the remains of the plaster frieze of the old front room can still be seen. By a strange coincidence No 31 is largely occupied by another building society, the Alliance Perpetual. What more heaven-sent name could commemorate that immortal partnership? Its yard is now no more, roofed over with glass these many years and overshadowed by a modern cloakroom, projecting on girders from an upper storey. But its outline can clearly be seen. The yard of No 34 still exists, hidden behind the same little mews premises between Nos 12 and 14 Kendalls Place. Although these buildings have been partially modernized, the electric lamp bracket occupies the same position on the wall as its Victorian predecessor.

Though we may never see that great statue of Holmes gazing down Baker Street, it would be a sad thing if the present orgy of bronze-casting were allowed to subside without some token being placed on those gallant walls that withstood in turn revolvers, air-guns, and arson. Perhaps a summit meeting of international Sherlockians could be convened in London. In that pleasant atmosphere squabbles concerning the table could be superfluous. It would, of course, be H-shaped! A boy having been sent down to Stanford's, the maps could be arrayed on it, lines drawn, and calculations checked and re-checked. At last the official recognition could be pronounced. That the evidence of 'The Back Yards of Baker Street' would be upheld, there is little doubt.

All this would be a relief. The fog would really have lifted. A cold wind may blow down Baker Street, 'such a wind as never blew on England yet—and a good many of us may wither before its blast'. But what matter? 'A cleaner, better, stronger land will lie in the sunshine when the storm has cleared.'

For Sherlockians—as for politicians, is that too much to ask?

Mr Davies' map on the end papers shows Baker Street in 1894 from Portman Mansions to George Street. It is based on the Ordnance Survey 5 foot Plans, Sheet VII/51. Second edition 1895. Re-surveyed 1893-4. (Slightly reduced.) Small black triangles indicate front-doors; black blobs with line indicate street lamps. First edition 1872, east side only and modern numbering inserted.

ANNEX

> ✦✦

R. IVAR GUNN

EXAMINATION PAPER

'Shall the examination proceed?' 'Yes, let it proceed, by all means.' *(The Three Students)*

1. (a) Who was a *danseuse* at the Allegro?
   (b) Who was a prima donna at the Imperial Opera of Warsaw?
   (c) Whose father conducted the orchestra at the old Imperial Theatre?
   (d) Whose father commanded the Sea of Azov fleet in the Crimea war?
   (e) Who had an aunt at Harrow?
   (f) Who had an aunt at Pinner?
   (g) Who paid far above the market price for a governess?
   (h) Who made a four-figure income by the paragraphs he contributed every week to the garbage papers?
   (i) Who was in the stand at Doncaster when it collapsed?
   (j) Who played Rugby football for Blackheath?
   (k) Who owned a Corot; a Greuze; a Kneller, a horse called Rasper, a dog called Carlo?
   (l) Whose boots had been resoled?

2. In the following list houses and their occupiers are jumbled. Assign each house by its letter to its proper occupier:
   (a) Hurlstone Manor House   Percy Phelps
   (b) Birlstone Manor House   Robert Furguson
   (c) Tuxbury Old Hall   Mr Williamson
   (d) Yoxley Old Place   Reginald Musgrave
   (e) Charlington Hall   Colonel Barclay
   (f) Deep Dene House   Professor Coram
   (g) Cheeseman's   Neville St Clair

179

(h) Briarbrae   John Douglas
(i) Lachine   Josiah Brown
(j) The Cedars, Lee   Colonel Emsworth
(k) Laburnam Lodge, Chiswick   Alexander Holder
(l) Fairbank, Streatham   Jonas Oldacre

3. Give the context of the following passages:
   (a) By George! It's attempted murder at the least. Nothing less will hold the London message boy.
   (b) I usually give up one day to pure amusement when I come to Town, so I spent it at the Museum of the College of Surgeons.
   (c) Have you dragged the basin of the Trafalgar Square fountain?
   (d) You cannot fail to be delighted with the traces of heredity shown in the p's and in the tail of the g's.
   (e) There is vacillation in his k's and self esteem in his capitals.
   (f) Oscillation upon the pavement always means an *affaire du coeur*.
   (g) There are some women in whom the love of a lover extinguishes all other loves, and I think that she must have been one.
   (h) He has never said anything. He is a perfect gentleman. But a girl always knows.
   (i) I call him a gentleman by courtesy, but he is quite a common-looking person.
   (j) You have less frontal development than I should have expected.
   (k) Your own exit is more likely to be in perpendicular than horizontal.
   (l) I believe that a single lady can get on very nicely upon an income of about sixty pounds.
   (m) It has always been my habit to hide none of my methods either from my friend Watson or from anyone who might take an intelligent interest in them.

4. What were the names and occupations of the Moriarty brothers? What person or places do you associate with the names of Moran and Hudson?

5. Whom do you associate with the following descriptions:
   (a) A dwindling *frou frou* of skirts.
   (b) A costume of dove-coloured silk with ostrich feather trimming.
   (c) The daintiest thing under a bonnet on this planet.
   (d) A little blonde woman . . . clad in some sort of light *mousseline-de-soie*, with a touch of fluffy pink chiffon at her neck and wrists.
   (e) A little, dark, silent person with suspicious and side-long eyes.
   (f) Her violet eyes shining, her lips parted, a pink flush upon her cheeks, all thought of her natural reserve lost in her overwhelming excitement and concern.
   (g) Tall, queenly, a perfect figure, a lovely mask-like face, with two wonderful Spanish eyes which looked murder at us both.
   (h) Her cheeks, though considerable freckled, were flushed with the exquisite bloom of the brunette, the dainty pink which lurks at the heart of the sulphur rose.
   (i) She was a well-grown young woman. I suppose you might say she was handsome. Perhaps some would say she was very handsome.

6. What tobacco did Dr Watson smoke? Who was his tobacconist? Who smoked Indian cigars, Dutch East Indian cigars, Egyptian cigarettes, Grosvenor mixture, long-cut Cavendish, a hookah? Who made his own cigarettes?

7. Who were the victims of yellow fever, brain fever, ichthyosis, diphtheria, short-sight, a summer cold, opium poisoning, carbon monoxide poisoning?

8. Who wrote on the following subjects:
   (a) The Kingdom of the Midianites.
   (b) The Documents in the Coptic monasteries of Syria and Egypt.
   (c) The Dynamics of the Asteroid.
   (d) The Book of Life.
   (e) Some Freaks of Atavism.
   (f) Three months in the jungle.
   Mention any references to the *Leeds Mercury*, the *Pink 'Un*, and the *Journal de Geneve*.

9. When did Sherlock Holmes visit Norway, Odessa, Montpelier, Florence, Bow Street Police Station, Doctor's Commons, the Russian Embassy in London? On what occasions did he draw deductions from spatulate fingers, bare feet, a pierced ear, a jagged ear, nose bleeding, a family portrait, railway points, pencil chips, an old boot, a dumb-bell?

10. Who stayed at the following hotels:
    (a) Englischer Hof at Baden.
    (b) Englischer Hof at Meirengen.
    (c) Hotel Escurial, Madrid.
    (d) Hotel Dulong, Lyons.
    (e) Langham Hotel.
    (f) Hotel Cosmopolitan.
    (g) Mexborough Private Hotel.
    (h) Dacre Hotel.
    (i) Brambletye Hotel.

11. What do you know of the Duke of Balmoral, Madame Lesurier, Matilda Briggs, Allardyce the Butcher, the Central Press Syndicate, 'our Merengo', the black Formosa Corruption, Pope's Court, Marcini's, the Tankerville Club? What weddings do you associate with St Saviour's, near King's Cross; St George's, Hanover Square; and St Monica's in the Edgware Road?

THE END